COMPUTER MESSAGE SYSTEMS

Data Communications Book Series

COMPUTER MESSAGE SYSTEMS

Jacques Vallee

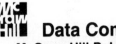

Data Communications
McGraw-Hill Publications Company
1221 Avenue of the Americas
New York, New York 10020

Project supervision was done by The Total Book.
The typesetter was Monotype Composition Company, Inc.
The cover was designed by Cathy Canzani, Design Works.
Kingsport Press, Inc. was printer and binder.

Computer Message Systems

1 2 3 4 5 6 7 8 9 0   KPKP   8 9 8 7 6 5 4

ISBN 0-07-606874-9

Library of Congress Cataloging in Publication Data

Vallee, Jacques.
        Computer message systems.

        (McGraw-Hill data communications book series)
        Bibliography: p.
        Includes index.
        1. Data transmission systems.   2. Computer networks.
3. Electronic mail systems.   4. Teleconferencing.
5. Videotex (Data transmission system)   I. Title.
II. Series.
TK5105.V35   1984   384   83-25208   115074
ISBN 0-07-606874-9

ABOUT
THE AUTHOR

Jacques Vallee was born and educated in France. He holds a Ph.D. in computer science from Northwestern University and worked at SHELL and RCA before joining Stanford University as manager of information systems in 1969. He later served as a principal investigator on ARPA and NSF projects to develop network-based message systems. In 1976 he founded the INFOMEDIA Corporation and served as chief executive officer until 1982, when he became associated with the San Francisco venture capital firm of Burr, Egan & Deleage, specializing in high-technology investments.

CONTENTS

ACKNOWLEDGMENTS

The greatest credit in the development of any new technology belongs not to the implementers but to the early users who take the risk of pioneering the application of an untested product in a new field. Much of what we have learned about computer-based message systems over the last ten years has come from such pioneers. Bradford Gibbs at NASA and Gerald Askevold at the U.S. Geological Survey have generously given their time and energy to this effort. Susan Wintersteen, Edwin Zebroski and Ron Simard at the Institute of Nuclear Power Operations, Paul Girard at Pacific Gas and Electric Company, Brian Shackel at the University of Birmingham, Denis Loveridge at Pilkington Glass, and Steve Costello have added considerably to our understanding of the field by launching and managing the first large-scale applications of computer conferencing outside the U.S. government.

Among those who have contributed to the development of the methodology described here, I owe special thanks to Robert Johansen, Hubert Lipinski, Kathleen Vian, and Thaddeus Wilson of The Institute for the Future; to Iris Schencke, Salvatore Suniga, Jean Dawson, Lindsey McLorg, Ruthie Smith, Carole Sciutto, Lorelei Zermani, and Jim and Jennifer O'Radnik at Infomedia Corporation; to Peter Peterson at Infomedia-Australia; to Robert Beebe, who developed JENNY; and to Richard Miller, architect of the NOTEPAD system.

I also wish to thank the people who have helped this effort through many personal discussions: notably Fred Weingarten and Connie McLindon at the National Science Foundation; Gary Wilcox and Robert Kupperman (who conceived the first computer conferencing system while at the Department of State); Ru-Ann Pengov at Hewlett-Packard; Robert Chartrand at the Congressional Research Service; Robert Harcharik at Tymnet; and Lawrence Roberts during his tenure at the Advanced Research Projects Agency (ARPA); as well as Paul Baran, Roy Amara, Tom Belden, Ray Williams, Terry Westgate, and Garry Shirts. May they find here my deep appreciation for their patience with me and their willingness to guide me through the maze of technical and management issues invariably raised by computer systems.

The project would not have been possible without the patience and expertise of Kathryn Redding and Annette Bodzin, who deciphered the many versions of the manuscript, and the efforts of Cheryl Weiner, who proved willing not only to consider the book at McGraw-Hill but also to manage its execution as well.

A very special thank you is in order for my wife Janine, who supported me valiantly throughout this project, and for my children Olivier and Catherine, who first encountered message systems as toys and have quickly outgrown a technology which still seems so mysterious to an older user like me.

Jacques Vallee

INTRODUCTION

People rarely buy computers in order to communicate. They buy computers to store and manage data and to handle transactions. Often computers are also used to compute, and to process text information. But the idea that a computer can be used to compose, exchange, and file messages is of recent introduction and has met with some resistance. Once the idea germinates, however, initial demonstration systems are rapidly outgrown. The range of applications of computer-based message systems is so vast and the impact on people and organizations so varied that simple systems are quickly outdated. Their data management capabilities prove inadequate, and their users demand new features and an increasing degree of interaction.

In recent years, computer-based message systems have become available on every major network in the United States. Many industrial organizations have either developed or bought electronic mail systems for internal use and are continually upgrading them. Some companies now provide both software packages and communication services to their clients, ranging from electronic mail to bulletin boards and computer conferencing. Systems for the general public are on the horizon, whether they are developed as packages on personal computers or as an integral part of new Videotex services.

Over the last ten years or so those who have followed the development of computer-based message systems have accumulated a large collection of documents that touch on every aspect of this field. As I started to read again through that mass of documents, I was surprised to see how the information sorted itself into three major categories that formed a natural structure for this book: the *need* for message systems, the *tools* of message systems, and the *management* of message systems.

Another surprise that awaits anyone reviewing this material is the rapidity of some of the changes. Much progress has been made since the timid early experiments using bulky terminals and unreliable computers linked through even more unreliable networks. In 1972 there was a community of less than 100 people who had been exposed to computer conferencing, most of them inside the government; and a few hundred who had used electronic mail in some form, most of them in the military. By the end of 1974, thanks to enlightened management at the Advanced Research Projects Agency of the Department of Defense (which funded ARPANET as the first national network linking computers of different makes) and at the National Science Foundation (which funded the FORUM project and the Electronic Information Exchange System at the New Jersey Institute of Technology), users numbered in the thousands, and industrial use began to develop. In FORUM, users untrained in computer use were able for the first time to send public and private messages to each other, to divide themselves into groups, and to file and retrieve conference information by topics.

Given this rapidly expanding interest in computer-based message systems, there was a need for a book that would define the various approaches and place them within the broader framework of group communications and decision making. The links to office automation and to other branches of computer technology had to be explained, and the methodologies available to assess the need for message systems and their impacts had to be surveyed (1).*

This book has been written for a wide audience that includes owners of personal computers who have an interest in communications; managers or executives of organizations concerned with the next level of office automation or integration; and software developers who need to improve their products while increasingly taking into account the human factors of computer-based communications. Finally, users themselves should find the book of interest because it is filled with actual examples and case studies they can relate to their own practical experience. The field is indeed old enough for a wide store of data to have accumulated about many real-world applications, some of them successful and others not. The lessons drawn from these applications had never before been summarized in one place.

Earlier I mentioned how quickly progress had been made. Today's computers and the networks linking them have become quite reliable. Terminals are now portable and cheap and it is possible to bring many of the functions of a message system closer to users if they are equipped with microcomputers. Furthermore, word processors have taken much of the burden of text editing and form generation away from the central system.

Ten years ago the exchange of electronic messages over computer networks was technically illegal, since it appeared to infringe upon the role of the post office or the common carriers. It was definitely a serious concern where international message exchange was concerned, and as late as 1981 the Japanese government did not allow the use of electronic mail systems from Japan, even over the network facilities of companies that qualified as international record carriers. These concerns have now disappeared as the dynamics of the entire communications industry broke down barriers against innovation and competition.

Along with this progress it is important to note the things that did *not* improve but, in fact, got worse over those 10 years. They constitute the third surprise I felt as I surveyed the material for this book. Computer networks, reliable as they have become, still present the user with bewildering complexity. They are difficult to

---

*Numbers in parentheses refer to the Annotated References at the end of the book.

comprehend, even for the trained technical specialist, and they confront the casual user with a lot of steps and jargon that in this day and age are simply an unnecessary obstacle. Much confusion still exists about the requirements for effective communications. One person calls "conferencing" what another calls "mail."

The human factors of communications are still largely ignored. As new companies get into the field, they hire the best programmers they can find to implement message systems. These programmers are often compiler writers or experts in operating systems and have had no experience in dealing with end users. They have operated in a completely different environment, where communications had a much narrower meaning. Some early successes have also had the unfortunate result of freezing the technical reality of the field for too long. Network mail on the ARPANET is a case in point. Introduced in the early 1970s, electronic mail systems have been very successful on the ARPANET, where they served a highly trained community of technical experts. When it came time to design new systems for wider communities, these same technical experts found it very difficult to be creative in ways that differed from what they had first learned.

Finally, the preconception that a message system is nothing more than just another application of computers (nothing more than text editing or graphics, for example) is a difficult one to change. Message systems are different because they do not fit within the theory of human–machine systems as we know it today. They are *systems for group interaction through machines*, the theory of which will be evolving over the next 20 years. Such systems involve all the elements depicted in Fig. I-1, where I have tried to show electronic mail, bulletin boards, and confer-

FIGURE I-1   The mosaic of technical subjects relevant to message systems. (Shaded: the area covered by this book.)

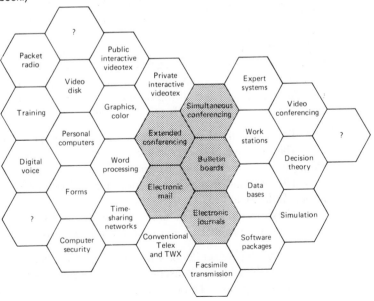

encing among the pieces of a mosaic that also includes data bases, programs, forms, word processing, stored digital voice, and video images.

Throughout this book I have tried to keep jargon to a minimum and avoid lengthy definitions. For instance, the term "computer message system" has been used, rather than the more cumbersome "computer-based message system," or CBMS, which may be more technically accurate. In describing applications and statistical results I have felt at liberty to draw heavily from my experience with systems such as PLANET, NOTEPAD, and JENNY as instances of more generic types of functions. This experience arose from an even earlier system which was called FORUM and was first implemented on ARPANET, the first large-scale computer network. From our experience with FORUM between 1973 and 1974 arose the PLANET system, which in turn led to NOTEPAD and to many of the observations made in this book. In the meantime, however, several other systems were implemented by research and business organizations to serve similar needs. Although some of their products are described in Part Two of this book, I have not had sufficient access to their user communities to draw detailed parallels.

Also in the name of simplicity I have not included a lengthy bibliography. The literature of the field changes very rapidly, and any attempt to be exhaustive is doomed to failure. I have only included those references that have a direct bearing on the arguments presented or which add an important level of detail to the information summarized. Numbers in parentheses within the text refer the reader to the Annotated References.

As early as 1975 my colleagues and I approached a major publisher with the concept of a book similar to the present one. He rejected our proposal with the comment that "technologically there are only two ingredients: a good network and a cheap enough terminal. The software is trivial to do." One of the lessons that led to the development of this book is that the software, unfortunately, is not trivial at all, because it needs to take into account a wider range of variables than programmers have previously encountered in their work. The level of effort involved in the implementation of a complete computer message system is similar to the work required to develop a large database system or a sophisticated operating system.

There are good reasons for the rapid expansion of computer message systems in industry: They make an important impact on the productivity of organizations that use them. This impact is felt in four ways:

1 These systems decrease the cost of running large projects.
2 They remove obstacles to the sharing of information and skills, thus eliminating production delays in the process.
3 They expand management control and facilitate reporting and tracking of project milestones.
4 They expand the range of access among teams separated by time and space, permitting the formulation and solution of new classes of problems.

It is from this observation—not of the specific features of the technology, but of its direct benefits to its users—that we begin as we describe first the need for message systems, then the available tools, and finally the means of managing them.

ONE

THE NEED FOR
MESSAGE SYSTEMS

## CHAPTER 1

A TECHNOLOGY FOR EFFECTIVE COMMUNICATION

MESSAGE SYSTEMS: A TECHNOLOGICAL AND SOCIAL LEAP

For the past 15 years computer technology and the communications field have been on a collision course. In organizations where letters, the phone, and Telex had been the dominant forms of management interaction, computers began to be used to handle remote transactions and to file memos. From there it was a simple step to sharing project information and exchanging electronic mail. At first this was accomplished by linking simple teletypes with timesharing computers (the term "timesharing" means simply that the central machine is capable of dividing its attention among several users, which makes possible simultaneous access from several remote locations). Later it became possible to buy or lease printing or display terminals with the capability to be linked electronically to a telephone line through a device called a *modem*. Some models include a coupler which accepts most telephone handsets. Since many of the terminals were portable, new styles of work became possible. An executive "on the move" could read his or her computer mail from a hotel room. A major concern of managers became the adaptation and integration of this new wave of technology into the behavior of office workers, engineers, and project leaders. It became possible to speculate on the impact this fusion of computer and communications would make on society at large. The range of technological opportunities—and problems—seemed to open widely.

As we begin this book it is important to underline one fact: The developments we have just described are only the beginning of a major restructuring of communications patterns. The way we interact as individuals and in groups, the way we pose problems and solve them, and the way we access data and argue about issues is going to be drastically affected by this transformation.

Furthermore, the technology will not stabilize in the near future. As soon as procedures are defined to allow computer terminals to access remote machines, the characteristics of the networks used to convey the data change. Users insist on entering their messages through word processors with increasing memory power and speed. Not only are terminals getting smaller and more portable, but an entire computer will now fit inside a briefcase. The age of portable computers with a flat display, a large memory, and a simple telephone connection has arrived.

Within existing organizations this wave of innovation is not universally welcomed. Middle managers are resisting changes that affect the way they have traditionally filtered information. The issue of management control in a world where everyone has potential access to everyone else is an unresolved problem. Lack of qualified office personnel to handle these new tools is an increasing concern.

For these reasons it would have been foolish to center this book strictly on the software aspects of computer message systems. These systems are computer programs designed to support a particular type of interaction among a particular group of people. Therefore, the human and social factors are the critical ones. The effectiveness of any system can be judged only when the total picture is understood. Among large companies a message system is only one component of "the integrated office." But the concept of the integrated (or automated) office is itself a moving target. Electronic components are changing rapidly, putting computer power and large storage at the disposal of everyone. As equipment manufacturers under-

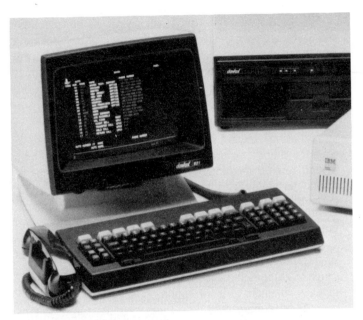

FIGURE 1-1a Some terminals, such as the Davox Series 921 Professional PC Desk Set, have a telephone connection on the side.

FIGURE 1-1b The Teleray Model 100/1500 is an example of a screen terminal requiring a separate phone coupler or "modem."

stand better the human factors of office work, the appearance of the machines used for word processing, computing, and data entry will continue to change. So will the skills required in their operation. The introduction of graphics and voice processing to systems initially designed for data will force major restructuring. Much of the innovation will be directed at products that will fail to capture a market and will end up in the garbage can.

No wonder managers have been slow in introducing new technology to the office. Faced with the need to retrain their personnel and new reporting patterns, middle managers are feeling especially vulnerable to a form of technical innovation whose benefits are potentially considerable but ill-defined on a short-term basis. The penetration of word processing equipment into the office has been much slower than initially expected by the industry. Penetration of message systems into large organizations is going to be an irreversible but necessarily slow process.

The social system we call "the office" was a major leap when it developed. Another enormous leap will be taken in the coming decade. But the new technology, impressive as it is, can be confusing for the typical clerical worker responsible for tasks involving limited judgment in large organizations—filing insurance claims, processing loan applications, issuing airline tickets. And it is at this level that communications systems will be tested. Such users generally lack a technical orientation.

Many surveys also question the English language skills among clerical workers of the future. Yet this same user of the future will need access to an expanding range of equipment capabilities and will be called upon to control multiple, simultaneous channels of information. A heavy investment in human factor skills, especially in training, will be mandatory as message systems are introduced. (Yet in the United States clerks already spend less than 1 year on a job, forcing rapid retraining.)

Finally, another difficulty faces both developers and users of computer-based message systems: It has to do with the difficulty in deploying an effective marketing force. Software companies may be successful in implementing message systems, but they may not know how to sell them, or to whom. And the user who has just purchased such a system may find the local vendor representative incapable of supporting it, and unable to understand or explain either its function or its impact. One of the goals of this book is to assist in bridging this gap.

Computer-based message systems represent a technology for effective communications, provided communications patterns are well-defined and the tools themselves are understood and brought under control. It is to these two issues that we will devote the balance of this first chapter.

COMMUNICATIONS PATTERNS

Let us begin with a simple-minded review of the three modes of communications open to "me" as an individual (Fig. 1-2). I can talk to myself (a form of communications often observed among managers), or I can talk to "you" in a person-to-person dialogue, or I can address "a group."

Communications can take place over six possible routes, depicted in Fig. 1-3. Three involve no delay: I can send information or receive it in real time; I can even send and receive simultaneously. More commonly, our communications involve delays: I can mail a letter or a memo without knowing when it will be received. I can watch a video tape without knowing when that tape was made. And the normal business situation finds me equipped with an in box and an out box where information is sent and received at variable rates.

Talking to myself

Talking to you

Talking to a group

FIGURE 1-2   Three modes of communications.

FIGURE 1-3   Six routes for human communications.

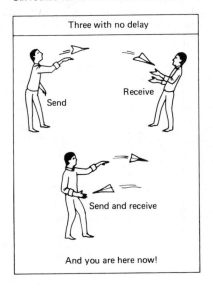

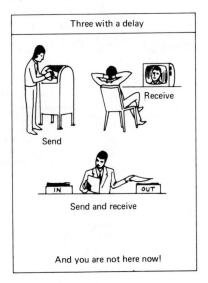

When combined (Fig. 1-4), these six communications routes and three communications modes form a simple matrix of communications patterns. For example, I can "talk to myself" through a file. I can exchange information with myself in the future through an agenda. I can send an order, receive a message, engage in real-time conversations. I can send mail (with delays) and receive questionnaires and forms to fill out. I can send and receive transactions and memos.

Let's look at the numbers. In the mid-1970s the total number of forms filled out in the United States reached about 200 billion. There were 112 billion memoranda and 17 billion transactions. No wonder the manufacturers of office automation equipment such as Xerox and IBM have concentrated on that part of our communications map! (See Figs. 1-5a and 1-5b.)

Computer-based message systems will clearly need to provide access to those areas of the map already computerized: file systems, databases, preestablished forms, word processing environments, and transaction-oriented networks. But they will also need to cover new functions to which computers have not traditionally been applied: handling real-time sending of instructions, simultaneous conferencing, group bulletin boards.

Along with this background on communications patterns, some definitions are in order.

We will call *computer mail* the use of a computer-based message system to compose, edit, send, and file person-to-person messages.

We will call *bulletin board* the use of a computer-based message system to post, file, and retrieve messages from an individual to a group, where the group is defined by the topic of all the messages.

We will call *electronic journal* the use of a computer-based message system to compose, send, review, and select pieces of text that can be published by a group of "editors" and retrieved by a community of "readers." What distinguishes the electronic journal from computer mail is the length of the average message, the review process to which it is subjected, and the intent of its publication.

FIGURE 1-4   Communications patterns.

	No delay			Delay		
	Send	Receive	Send and receive	Send	Receive	Send and receive
Talking to myself				File		Agenda
Talking to you	Message	Order	Conversation	Mail	Questionnaire	Transactions
Talking to a group	Address	Report	Conference	Article	Form	Memo

Databases

	No delay			Delay		
	Send	Receive	Send and receive	Send	Receive	Send and receive
Talking to myself				File		Agenda
Talking to you	Message	Order	Conversation	Mail	Question- naire	Transaction
Talking to a group	Address	Report	Conference	Article	Form	Memo

Text editors   Electronic mail

FIGURE 1-5a   Areas of communications that computers are already supporting.

	No delay			Delay		
	Send	Receive	Send and receive	Send	Receive	Send and receive
Talking to myself				File		Agenda
Talking to you	Message	Order	Conversation	Mail	Question- naire	Transactions
Talking to a group	Address	Report	Conference	Article	Forms	Memos

Computer-based message systems

FIGURE 1-5b   Areas of communications supported by computer message systems.

We will call *computer conferencing* the use of a computer-based message system to define groups of people sharing access to a common topic file through which both public and private messages are exchanged.

Computer conferencing can be effected either in "extended" fashion—when messages are exchanged by the group over a period of days, weeks, or months— or in "simultaneous" fashion—when all users are at their terminals at the same time and can read messages as soon as they are composed and released by the sender. Simultaneous exchange of messages is sometimes referred to as *synchronous conferencing*.

The above definitions clearly provide for several areas of overlap. For example, a mail system can be used to support bulletin boards. A conferencing system can be viewed as an extension of mail, or it can be bent into an electronic journal. At the present state in our understanding of computer-based message systems, the definitions we have given simply describe four types of behavior in the much larger space of communications needs. However, as we will see in later sections, this field is now old enough so that the four types of systems have already acquired certain standard characteristics which the designer and the user have to keep in mind when they are faced with a specific communications task.

Before we go any further into our discussion of these systems, it is useful to review the various forms taken by the technology that supports them.

THE TECHNOLOGY AND ITS COST

Discussions between communications users and technologists are often futile because they argue about the feasible instead of focusing on the practical. We have the technology today to install, maintain, and link together a hundred word processors on the moon, but the project would hardly be termed practical. Yet this kind of adventure is similar to what we see in many companies: computer technology deployed at the wrong time, for the wrong reason, at the wrong place, and very often at an exaggerated cost, where a much simpler approach could have given more significant results. At other times, companies have stumbled upon imaginative uses of existing systems and have opened the way to new developments that "experts" in the field had completely failed to predict.

In the following pages, then, we will review available technology options that have an impact on computer-based message systems, but we will keep this review within the context of cost and practicality considerations. As a backdrop to this discussion, let us remember that Telex operates at 10 to 15 characters per second, and rates range from $100 to $300 an hour. An ordinary telegram costs $6 for the first 15 words plus 20 cents per word over that limit.

Computer Terminals

We have shown in Fig. 1-1*b* a standard form of "dumb" computer terminals. These devices cost between $700 and $1500, and are capable only of displaying or printing out information as it is received. They have no memory. They must be attached to expensive mainframes or minis.

While some terminals have a built-in telephone coupler and modem (which makes the data stream understandable to a telephone line), others do not, and it is the user's responsibility to purchase that equipment separately. Typically, the communication will take place at 300 baud, or 300 bits per second, which corresponds to the display of 30 characters per second, which is close to the rate at which most people can read. More advanced equipment accommodates rates of 1200 baud (120 characters per second). The higher speed means more expensive equipment but entails a saving in terms of communication time. The size of most displays allows 24 lines of 80 characters.

Word Processors

These machines are self-contained and cost from $3000 to $15,000 and have a bewildering set of features, settings, and requirements. Very often they are restricted in their communication capabilities, permitting only interaction with devices of the same make. When they can be utilized as user stations in a computer-based message system, they have an advantage over terminals since a user can compose his or her text, save it as a file, and edit that file before actually establishing a connection to a central message system. The user can then send the whole message file as a burst of information. The connection demands that the central service be specially programmed to accept communication from that particular make of word processor, and that the user adhere to certain standards; in particular, that the message file should be free of special formatting characters, which vary from one manufacturer to another.

Portable Computers

Recently several companies have placed on the market devices that are similar in size and appearance to portable terminals but offer considerable memory and computing power. These machines cost between $2000 and $9000 and feature flat screen displays that allow the entire computer to fold into a small box. Some are battery-powered and provide a telephone connection. The major drawback at present is the size of the screen, currently limited to 8 lines of 40 characters, although the more expensive systems allow the full screen of 24 lines and 80 characters, which supports message exchange most effectively. Examples of these are Grid, Radio Shack, Kaypro, and Gavilan.

Personal Computers

By 1985 industry estimates project there will be 6 million personal computers in the United States, made by such companies as Apple, IBM, Commodore, Tandy, and Atari. While they are bought for a variety of applications, ranging from VisiCalc to video games, these devices have communications capabilities, and the demand for new interactive services defines one of the fastest-growing business sectors in the computer industry.

The typical personal computer in a business or home setting costs from $2000 to $10,000 and may have large storage devices (5 or 10 megabytes) as well as removable diskettes. A printer is attached, and both black-and-white and color displays are supported.

To enable this device to be connected to a remote computer, one generally needs to purchase the communications card, the modem, and a special software program to handle the data stream.

Videotex Terminals

While most message systems available today have grown as timesharing applications in the traditional data processing culture, another form of information delivery has been growing in Europe and Japan in the midst of considerable confusion. This form of delivery is called Videotex and aims at providing the home user with new services such as shopping, banking, and database consultation through the two electronic devices already available in the home: either a cable or the telephone and the TV set. This is a market for large companies, with heavy involvement by government regulators. In the United States, firms such as AT&T, Warner, and Knight-Ridder have made large investments in preliminary experiments.

The user of a Videotex system would lease or buy a keyboard with a microcomputer which is preprogrammed for the services to be accessed. The interaction is very simple (usually limited to menu choices) and the output is in color, with simple graphics. As we shall see later on, service providers have avoided the issue of message systems under Videotex. The keyboards themselves are generally not designed to permit convenient entry of text by the user; rather, it is thought that the customer will want only to make simple choices among prepackaged, prestructured information files which are centrally controlled by a large organization.

Computer Networks

During the 1960s it became possible not only to connect remote users to a central computer but also to link the computers themselves together. Most computer-based message systems today use a network of some kind, often a commercially available public network, where the price of the connection is measured by duration and by the number of characters transmitted. Costs range between $2 and $10 per hour, depending on the time of day and sophistication and reliability of service.

A computer network is commonly based on a number of service centers connected by high-speed telephone lines. In this country the phone lines are usually leased from AT&T. The network architecture is based on two kinds of special minicomputers: The *node* that processes the phone calls from remote users is simply a terminal concentrator and a gateway to the network itself. As a terminal concentrator, it is capable of aggregating information coming from different places, and also of taking the stream of data coming from a computer and breaking it into units going back to the proper locations. As a gateway, it handles the routing of the information to the place where it can be processed. When a user calls one of the local access telephone numbers, that person is actually calling a network node which will route messages to the proper computer.

The computer receives the message through another specialized machine called a *network processor*. It is this machine which permits a computer of one type to "understand" messages or files coming from a computer or terminal of a different manufacturer.

The computers providing service on the network are often called "hosts." If the computer is "down," the network processor will inform users that the "host" is not responding, or is "shut."

Major network companies are General Electric, Tymnet, Control Data, GTE/ Telenet, and ADP. Their services vary greatly. Some will interconnect their clients' computers. Others are exclusively designed to provide service on their own computers. Some of the networks are regulated as common carriers. That is the case in particular for Telenet and for Tymnet. The rates they apply have to be approved by the FCC and vary depending on the location (high or low population density) from which the call is made.

Utilization of a network is limited by the number of telephone lines that the local *node* can handle and by the number of access paths or "ports" into the particular computer being used. If the network is saturated, a user may get a message such as "All circuits busy."

In the exchange of messages shown between users A and B in Fig. 1-6, six computers are involved: two nodes, two network processors, and the hosts they are serving. It is the programmer's job to make this architecture as transparent as possible to the users of the system.

Local Area Networks

Within a single business organization the need exists to connect together all the word processors and microcomputers that share the same information. This is accomplished by giving all these devices access to a common link through a standard protocol. This requires one more interface device and a cable that runs through the entire building. The price of the interface device can reach $1000 per unit, connected, but will be dropping rapidly in the next few years.

A local area network makes it possible, among other things, to keep all important data files on a separate disk device and to allow remote users to tap into this

FIGURE 1-6   Simplified topology of a computer network.

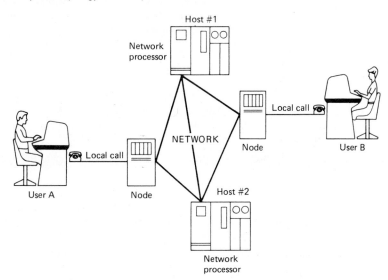

large storage. Various experts disagree on the protocols that should be used to implement local area networks. In particular, IBM is working on standards that differ from those of other manufacturers. The implementation of integrated message systems on local area networks is naturally vulnerable to the selection of such a standard architecture.

Advanced Workstations

Given the ability to integrate computing power with storage and communications in a single device, it is but one step to the definition of a complete "workstation" for executives. Such a workstation is basically a powerful personal computer having special functions such as the handling of voice and graphics and an additional audio channel. Terminals and portable computers that combine voice and data are already available. Stored digital images can also be interfaced with the workstation.

Digitized Voice

The human voice is the most natural support for communication, but it requires considerable time for the sending and receiving of a message. Speech is slow and comprehension can be unreliable. The technology exists today, however, to capture a message from a speaker, digitize it, and store it. Delayed access to this message can then be provided, so that multiple recipients can pick it up at their convenience.

The productivity gains from the use of this technique are obvious, since "telephone tag" can be avoided, at least for the communication of information that does not require an immediate acknowledgment or the resolution of an issue.

The drawbacks of voice mail—as compared to text messages—are also fairly obvious. It is impossible to scan, prioritize, or retrieve on the basis of key words, and there is no convenient interface with printing or the display of information. Companies in the voice mail business include IBM, AT&T, Rolm, ECS, and others.

Cellular Radio

The technologies discussed so far are all based in one way or another on the use of telephone lines. Yet the equipment exists today to enable users of portable computers to communicate over radio waves. It was first used commercially in the early 1970s when Bell developed a "cellular" system, so called because a major city could be divided into small sections, each equipped with its own low-power radio transmitter.

Some organizations—such as the police—have long used radio communications. But this is supported by a single high-power transmitting tower wired to the local phone network. The tower has a range of only about 50 miles on very few channels, which is discouraging to users.

Industry analysts are divided on the subject of the growth of cellular radio.

(Cartoon by Boro, courtesy of the San Francisco Business Journal, 1982.)

The existence of a large market for these devices has not been demonstrated, and much concern exists over regulatory and technical issues. But the fact remains that wireless transmission of information is a natural support for computer-based message systems in the future.

Case Study 1: Institute of Nuclear Power Operations (INPO)

Our first case study introduces a community of users who have linked together many different organizations around the world through a sophisticated computer message system. The applications are varied and cover a wide range of activities within the community. The central need, however, is access to rapidly changing information contributed by other members of the community and the ability to retrieve and document actions taken in response to physical events, mechanical failures, and management decisions or regulatory changes.

Given this background, Case Study 1 illustrates the technology and its cost.

A few days after the accident at Three Mile Island (TMI), representatives of the electric utility industry met in Chicago to reorganize the handling of nuclear safety issues in the United States. The group asked the Electric Power Research Institute (EPRI) to take the lead in the coordination of all safety information and analysis data. Formed several years ago as a "think tank" funded by all the utility companies, EPRI has established its headquarters in Palo Alto and conducts research projects in all areas of energy production, from coal and nuclear energy to solar power.

It was in the aftermath of Three Mile Island that EPRI created the Nuclear Safety Analysis Center (NSAC), directed by Dr. Edwin Zebroski, with Dr. Ron Simard as coordinator of nuclear safety information. NSAC turned to the use of computer conferencing among the major centers of the electric utility industry. In the *NSAC Industry Report* for September 1979, a newsletter that reached 7000 subscribers, EPRI announced the availability of the service:

NSAC's New Safety Data Available on Dial-Up Basis

All utilities participating in NSAC activities may now obtain the very latest schedule of forthcoming meetings and summaries of important documents in the NSAC information file, by means of their own remote computer terminal. Notification of significant events in operating plants will be added as this analysis develops.

The new service, called NOTEPAD, is a computer-based communications service accessible throughout the United States and Canada, and parts of Western Europe and the Far East. Users dialing the nearest NOTEPAD number by commercial telephone lines are checked by the computer in Palo Alto which is programmed to be able to sort out material previously scanned so that only new material in each category needs to be reviewed.

A user manual and password authorization system to provide security of access for each user are provided.

In September 1979, operation of NOTEPAD began with 12 utilities on the system. The number gradually expanded as participants in other companies were trained to use computer conferencing. As the regulatory agencies and other studies keep pointing to the lack of group communication within the industry as a major factor in the crisis that followed the Three Mile Island accident, the importance of having a record of all safety-related information on a continuous basis had become obvious. NOTEPAD not only provides a permanently searchable record but also permits the intervention of experts and decision makers anywhere in the country. It also gives an audit trail of events leading to any major decision.

Four years later, NUCLEAR NOTEPAD is linking 70 utilities in the United States and 12 foreign utilities, notably Canada, France, and Japan. The information is under the control of the Institute of Nuclear Power Operations in Atlanta, Georgia—the organization which took over the mission of the Nuclear Safety Analysis Center.

Not only was NOTEPAD a useful substitute for many face-to-face meetings, it was a crisis management tool as well. It also allowed the industry to respond to regulatory requirements requested by federal authorities, resulting in numerous design changes and equipment modifications. One important fact about the TMI accident is that another plant, operated by another utility, had experienced the same type of component failure. In that case, which had taken place a year earlier, the operators of the plant had been able to control and correct the situation, but their experience was not recorded and distributed in such a way that other nuclear plants could benefit from it when they were faced with a similar problem.

Taking note of this fact, the Presidential Commission on TMI stated:

> There must be a systematic gathering, review and analysis of operating experience at all nuclear power plants coupled with an industry-wide international communications network to facilitate the speedy flow of information to affected parties.

The use of computer conferencing was the most effective way to respond to this requirement. The utility companies also had a major incentive to join the network: When a nuclear power plant is shut down, it costs $300,000 per day to replace the lost electricity. And design changes mandated as a result of the analysis of TMI cost about $20 million per plant.

Figure 1-7 shows a typical printout as an individual user would enter NUCLEAR NOTEPAD. Since the user has different interests, he or she belongs to several groups or activities, which are displayed on the menu. An asterisk next to

FIGURE 1-7   NUCLEAR NOTEPAD: Sample printout from INPO user's terminal.

```
The following activities are available to you:
   1.    Emergency hotline
*  2.    Operating plant experience
   3.    Significant event reports
   4. →  Operations and maintenance information
*  5.    Emergency planner information
*  6. →  Radiological protection information
   7.    Quality assurance information
   8.    Control room design information
Please type the number of the activity you wish to join
#
```

the activity title indicates that the new information has been entered and is waiting for that participant, either as a personal note or as a public message. An arrow indicates that another user is currently online in that same activity.

Again, according to a report by Dr. Simard, this illustrates the crucial difference between conferencing and simple messaging: A computer conference is a shared communication space:

> Up to 32 users may simultaneously access an activity and "conference" as they would face-to-face. Each user can make a public statement or can write personal messages to one or more of the others. Moreover, they have common access to computer programs which can be linked to the conference slot in memory. These programs are run and the results displayed to each user in real time. Finally, at the end of the conference, each user has a permanent record of all public messages and private messages addressed to him. These are kept on a disk for an indefinite period and can be searched by author, date ranges, and by specified character strings.

By 1981 there were 400 individuals from 100 organizations using the system. The level of usage was such that a message was seen by some of the participants within minutes and by most of the community within 48 hours. Since each user frequently copied and distributed relevant messages to others in his or her group, a request for information was rapidly circulated throughout the industry.

When a reactor in Arkansas developed trouble shortly after the system was made available, the NSAC representative at Arkansas Power & Light Company entered the information into his NOTEPAD terminal. Within 2 hours he had received help from other group members who had successfully dealt with similar problems in the past. He was able to take detailed information directly from NOTEPAD to assist in the solution of the incident.

Average monthly usage in terms of sessions at the terminal, connect hours, and message traffic is summarized in Fig. 1-8, which indicates that the average user finds new information in four or five of the activities available on the menu. A public message is read by 200 persons. The profile of this average user is further described in Fig. 1-9: He or she consults NOTEPAD once a day and in a period of 12 minutes receives 14 public messages and an unknown number of private notes. This level of activity translates into some simple cost considerations. Dr. Simard observes:

> Our average user is an engineer, probably capable of typing between two and four characters per second at his terminal. Thus, when he sends a private message to another individual, it will cost, typically, 40 to 80 cents to generate the message, and one to five cents to read it. Public messages, however, are usually longer and more expensive. A

FIGURE 1-8   Average monthly usage. (*Source: R. Simard.*)

Number of terminal sessions:	4,000
Number of activities accessed:	18,000
Number of connect hours:	1,000
Number of public messages sent:	800
Number of private messages sent:	2,000
Number of messages read:	164,000

> * Sees 10 activities on his menu
> * Logs into NOTEPAD once per day
> * Goes into four or five of his activities
> * Spends 12 minutes logged in
> * Receives 14 public messages and several private messages

FIGURE 1-9 The average user. (*Source: R. Simard.*)

one-page, single-spaced business letter typed by the same user might cost $4.50 to $8.00 to generate. If the typing were done off-line, or if a word processor operator prepared the message for streamed input, the cost of generation could be as low as $1.00. It would then be read by another user at a cost of 30 to 60 cents, depending upon his terminal speed.

At this writing the use of the system has expanded to include a larger number of organizations, and it has become necessary to make changes in the program to allow for 1000 users to have access to the same activity. NUCLEAR NOTEPAD represents the first use of a computer conferencing system to establish a permanent information link among an industrial community, cutting across company boundaries in more than a hundred different organizations.

## CHAPTER 2

THE MESSAGE ENVIRONMENT: THE ORGANIZATION, ITS MANAGEMENT, ITS CULTURE

CHARACTERISTICS OF ORGANIZATIONS

There is no such thing as an abstract message system without reference to the organization in which it operates. The same system which will be effective within company A could bring disaster to company B. Much of the discussion among designers of such systems regarding which particular set of features is "better" is frivolous. One must start from the environment to determine which type of system has the best chance of being accepted and used.

Questions to be asked at this level include: Is the organization centralized or decentralized? Is there a single purpose to its use, or will it have to accommodate many different groups? Does the information in the messages have long-term value? Is there a predetermined path for information within this community? Do users require simultaneous access to the information and to each other, or is message exchange effected on an extended basis?

To illustrate the scope of answers to these questions, we will discuss the classification of organizational structures and then we will describe briefly a number of actual environments, together with their unique constraints.

Figure 2-1 shows the four types of organization structures most frequently encountered. They are the *star*, the *wheel*, the *matrix*, and the *hierarchy*.

In a star-shaped organization a single individual or function sends orders to a

FIGURE 2-1   Four types of organization structures.

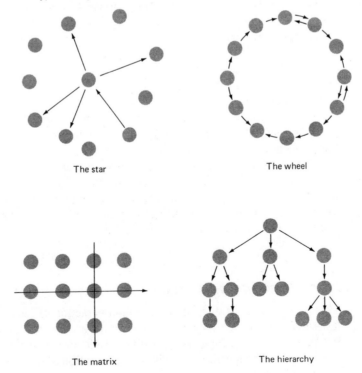

The star

The wheel

The matrix

The hierarchy

number of isolated recipients who have no need (and generally no means) to communicate among themselves. A sales region is often organized as a star, with the sales manager at the center.

In a wheel structure all participants are equal and no one plays a central role. Individuals in the group have equal access to each other. The community of all users of a particular database service constitutes such a wheel structure. So do all the banks that subscribe to SWIFT, the electronic funds transfer system, since at any time any bank can send a money order to any other subscriber.

In matrix organizations each individual is part of two activities: one dictated by the branch of the organization to which he or she reports, and one defined by his or her function, or role within a project that cuts across many branches. Numerous large companies are organized in this fashion. Thus, a research chemist in the detergents division of a personal products company could also be part of a research project on polymers through which he would report to a colleague from the paper division—while detergents are paying his salary.

The hierarchy is the most frequent form of industrial organization: to the president report several vice presidents, each one with his or her directors, to whom a number of managers and other subordinates report.

The armed forces have organized their communications along hierarchical lines. If an ensign in charge of military retirement programs for the Navy in Pearl Harbor needs to send a message to a captain assigned the same job with the U.S. Army in Frankfurt, the message is routed all the way up to the office of the admiral commanding the Pacific Fleet, who sends it to the Commanding General of American Forces in Europe. From there it goes all the way down to the captain in question. Clearly this environment will have some unique needs that a message system cannot ignore.

To make sure that the essential characteristics of the organizations to be served have been taken into account, we have designed two forms that reflect the profile of the organization itself (Fig. 2-2) and of the application under study (Fig. 2-3). Questions on the two forms are trying to determine a single central issue: Is a computer-based message system simply something which would be nice to have in this application, or is it really indispensable? Computer systems which are nice to have typically do not get used very much, because people are too busy in their daily routines to learn a new set of skills. There must be some stronger motivation than simply better communications. Some economic value must be attached to the improvement of interaction among the group. This motivation must be clearly perceived by every participant.

GROUP INTERACTION AND PARTICIPATION PATTERNS

There are certain constant patterns in the interaction of human groups. These patterns may be affected by the introduction of a computer-based message system, but they are not fundamentally changed by it. Some of the most stable patterns have to do with leadership and with the distribution of participation rates. They are observed both in business and in nonbusiness groups.

```
┌─────────────────────────────────────────────────────────────────┐
│                                                                   │
│  Name: _____    Size:  No. of branches _____ │
│                                                                   │
│  Location _____           Total personnel _____ │
│                                                                   │
│  Profit/nonprofit _____           Yearly budget _____  │
│                                                                   │
│  Industry field _____                                   │
│                                                                   │
│                                                                   │
│  Component or division _____    Contact persons, titles       │
│                                     and roles                     │
│  Structure _____                                   │
│                                                                   │
│  Function _____                                   │
│                                                                   │
│                                                                   │
│  Objectives of this group _____ │
│                                                                   │
│  _____ │
│                                                                   │
│  Management needs and concerns: _____ │
│                                                                   │
│  _____ │
│                                                                   │
│  Types of communication to be supported: _____ │
│                                                                   │
│  Check appropriate boxes:    ☐ Management information             │
│                              ☐ Policy discussion                  │
│                              ☐ Reporting                          │
│                              ☐ Data recording                     │
│                              ☐ Decision-making                    │
│                              ☐ Emergency management               │
│                              ☐ Dissemination of information       │
│                                                                   │
│  Leadership style: _____ │
│                                                                   │
│  Size of the group: _____                         │
│                                                                   │
│  Communication style: public/private _____         │
│                                                                   │
│  Group network topology: star — wheel — matrix — hierarchy        │
│                                                                   │
│  Evaluation requirements: _____ │
│                                                                   │
│  _____ │
│                                                                   │
│  Criteria for success of the message system in this organization: │
│                                                                   │
│  _____ │
│  _____ │
│  _____ │
│  _____ │
│  _____ │
│  _____ │
│                                                                   │
└─────────────────────────────────────────────────────────────────┘
```

FIGURE 2-2   Organization profile.

The first pattern that characterizes human interaction in groups—and this is relevant to the subject of message systems—has to do with the various *categories* of messages or utterances.

In the name of efficiency it is easy to fall into the trap of regarding all messages as *substantive*—in other words, that the group will discuss only the particular subject it has gathered to resolve is easy to assume. In practice, however, groups need at least three other categories or levels of discourse to be comfortable with the interaction and to conduct business effectively. For convenience in observing group interaction, we have tabulated comments having to do with management or *administration* separately from the *substantive* category, although such messages are closely related to the matter at hand, the subject of the communications.

```
┌────────────────────────────────────────────────────────────────┐
│                                                                  │
│   APPLICATION TYPE:   Project Management                         │
│                       Operating Management                       │
│                       Coordination Management                    │
│                       Consulting                                 │
│                       Research and Development                   │
│                       Service to an Industry                     │
│                       Service to a Community                     │
│   OBJECTIVES OF THIS APPLICATION:                                │
│   _____   │
│   _____   │
│   _____   │
│                                                                  │
│   WHY IS THE MESSAGE SYSTEM INDISPENSABLE?                       │
│   _____   │
│   _____   │
│   _____   │
│                                                                  │
│   HOW WILL THE MESSAGE SYSTEM SUPPLEMENT OTHER MEDIA?            │
│   _____   │
│   _____   │
│   _____   │
│   _____   │
│   _____   │
│                                                                  │
│   INITIAL GROUP MEMBERSHIP:  (Include names of group leaders)    │
│   _____      _____      _____                  │
│   _____      _____      _____                  │
│   _____      _____      _____                  │
│   _____      _____      _____                  │
│   _____      _____      _____                  │
│                                                                  │
│   ACCESS REQUIREMENTS:                                           │
│   Internal telephone system: _____   │
│   Local network access: _____   │
│   National network: _____   │
│   International network: _____   │
│   TERMINAL EQUIPMENT TO BE USED:                                 │
│   Dumb terminals (CRT or printers): _____    │
│   Intelligent terminals: _____    │
│   Personal computers: _____    │
│   Word processors: _____    │
│   TRAINING SCHEDULE:                                             │
│   _____   │
│   _____   │
│                                                                  │
└────────────────────────────────────────────────────────────────┘
```

FIGURE 2-3   Application profile.

One of the nonsubstantive levels might be called the *social* level. It has to do with greetings, jokes, pleasantries, and asides that define the context of the group situation. Social messages constitute the glue that holds the group together. Attempts to eliminate or reduce this form of communications will result either in failure of the group process or in the displacement of the social activity in a different form.

Another nonsubstantive category might be called *procedural*. Before they can discuss issues, groups need to agree on rules: Who is going to lead the discussion, what special roles are needed, who will keep the agenda, who can propose new subjects?

Yet another category is best called *learning*. It has to do with messages such as, "Does everyone hear me?" or, "How can I send a message so that only one person sees it?" or, "How can we recall the data we recorded last week on this subject?"

An example of the distribution of messages in a computer conference is given in Fig. 2-4. This was a conference of educators sponsored by the Kettering Foundation. Over half the messages were substantive, but about one-fifth were administrative and one-fifth were social. There was no procedural category recorded.

Another pattern that characterizes human interaction has to do with *participation rates*.

It has been widely observed that members of a group rarely participate equally in a discussion. Instead, we find that one or two individuals make over half of all the comments (or statements or messages) in a group process. The others participate according to a well-defined decreasing curve. This phenomenon, first described by Zipf in his book *Human Behavior* (2), has been verified many times. It applies to computer message systems as well.

To illustrate this process we can take one of Shakespeare's plays, such as *The Taming of the Shrew*, and tabulate the statements made by each character. The results for Act V (which contains 168 statements) are shown in Fig. 2-5.

We can perform the same analysis on a message system and observe a similar distribution. For example, the computer conference shown in Fig. 2-6 was held in 1974 among Canadian and U.S. experts discussing travel–communications trade-offs. In this particular conference, one user sent almost 30 percent of all entries. The top two participants sent over 40 percent of all messages.

The implications of this pattern are clear: The introduction of a computer-based message system does not change the behavior of human groups. Social activity needs to be preserved and the group will continue to be dominated by a few indi-

FIGURE 2-4   Typical distribution of messages among four content categories.

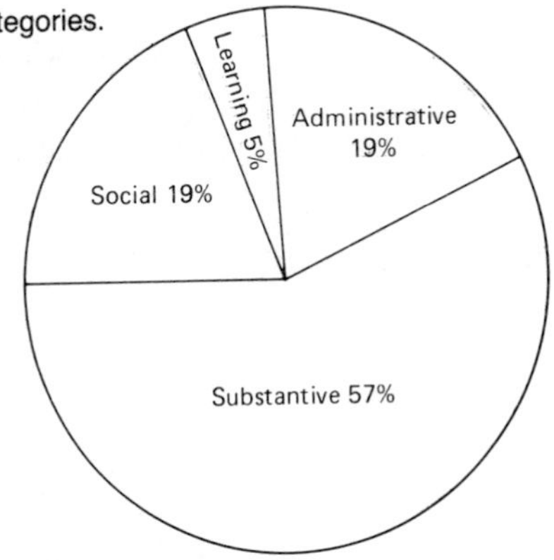

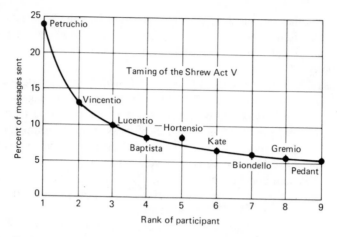

FIGURE 2-5   Typical distribution of participation in a face-to-face group.

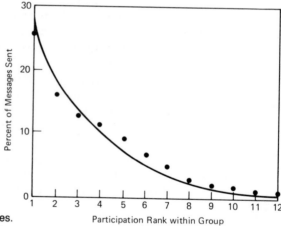

FIGURE 2-6   Typical distribution of participation rates.

viduals. Although the *opportunity* for communications has been greatly expanded, the message system must conform to a number of rather subtle human factors in order to be effective.

THE CULTURE OF THE ORGANIZATION

In the minds of business persons and scientists, the word "culture" is often associated with beautiful and useless things like ballet and broken Indian jars. It is not something they consider in the everyday reality of the office or the lab. Managers and executives have an especially hard time believing that a company possesses its own peculiar culture—not measured in the number of color photographs on the wall of the board room but in the pattern of communications within the firm, its unwritten rules, its special jargon, its symbols of power or status, its artifacts, and

HIGH CONTEXT

Greater tolerance for ambiguity
More emphasis on nonverbal
 communication
Responsibility based on agreement,
 not on contract
Implicit control
Group orientation
Relative values
Feelings and emotions
Wholistic concern

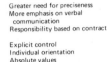

LOW CONTEXT

Greater need for preciseness
More emphasis on verbal
 communication
Responsibility based on contract

Explicit control
Individual orientation
Absolute values
Logics
Segmented concern

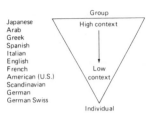

Japanese
Arab
Greek
Spanish
Italian
English
French
American (U.S.)
Scandinavian
German
German Swiss

FIGURE 2-7   High- and low-context cultures.

its rituals. Designers of a message system ignore this culture of the organization at their own risk.

The problem of dealing with organizational culture is made especially difficult because of a lack of a simple effective classification scheme for cultures. Anthropologists have been busy developing such schemes for many decades, of course; but the schemes are too complex for the average pragmatic engineer to be able to use as a guide.

One simple approach to the classification of cultures is Vincent Miller's idea of "context" (3). A *low-context culture* such as the United States or Germany emphasizes explicit control—great need to be precise, and an individual orientation of decisions. In a *high-context culture* such as the Japanese or Arab culture, on the contrary, there is greater tolerance for ambiguity—control is implicit and there is greater group orientation. Figure 2-7 summarizes these differences.

These cultural differences can be readily translated into management styles, which are a mirror of the social values and aspirations of the culture around the company. Figure 2-8 shows how people conduct business in high and low cultures.

If we return to some of the examples given earlier, we would classify the armed forces, with their hierarchical communication system, as a low-context culture, while financial investment represents a high-context culture where many decisions "emerge" from collective consultation.

Both high-context and low-context cultures need computer-based message systems, but these systems will be structured in very different ways. In one case, we may see an emphasis on electronic mail of the simplest kind to convey orders and process report forms. In another case, we will expect heavy use of bulletin boards, computer conferences, and group-oriented tools such as voting.

FIGURE 2-8   Characteristics of business cultures.

HIGH CONTEXT

No clear-cut delineation between functions
No job description
Greater need for coordination
Decision "emerged" collectively
Responsibility held collectively
Harmony and cooperation
Long term benefits
Emphasis of role over function
Bring job to person
Generalist oriented
Multiple skill development

LOW CONTEXT

Clear-cut delineation between functions
Job description
Greater need for self-assertion
Decision "made" by individual
Responsibility held by individual
Confrontation and competition
Short term gains
Function and role identical
Bring person to job
Specialist oriented
Single skill development

What does this mean in terms of network structure? It can be argued that in a high-context culture the idea of conferencing or of electronic mail in a wheel network will be a natural one. In a low-context American-type culture there may be a greater affinity for star networks and systems that broadcast orders from executives to those reporting to them.

Two observations from videoconferencing and from voice mail reinforce this argument. The businesses where voice mail has been successful are those where individual managers needed to make their decisions known to their group. The recipients of the messages were mainly expected to listen. If they responded, it was generally to report information back to the boss. Similarly, initial applications of videoconferencing technology in business have emphasized broadcasting of information by top management to disseminated locations. Product announcements by Ford or Hewlett-Packard executives to their branch managers and dealers are typical. These organizations have used the technology to reinforce their structure of star networks and to go in the direction of lower context. In the videoconferencing applications mentioned above, remote locations can respond only by telephone. Thus, technology can be used to formalize certain hierarchical differences.

Computer message systems can support any kind of structure. The richest information environment is created by group-oriented, high context network organizations, but many existing industrial structures do not need an elaborate conference facility and can be satisfied with simple message exchange.

Matching the medium to the real needs of the user organization is the most

FIGURE 2-9   Major benefits of a message system within a large organization.

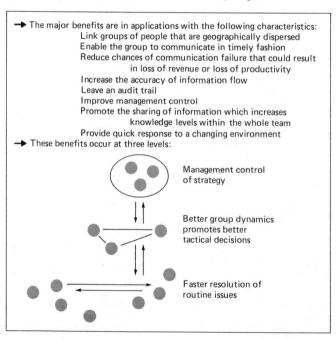

important part of designing a computer-based message system. The care with which this task is accomplished will define how successfully the system will be used. An awareness of the culture of the organization is required to create an effective match.

A SIMPLE TEST

We conclude this chapter with a quick test of the need for a message system within *your* organization. Think of a project on which you have been working with a number of your peers, one which requires communications. Then answer each question quickly in the sequence indicated. There are nine questions and they have either three or four possible answers. At the end of the test we will add up your answers.

THE FIVE-MINUTE "NEED" TEST

In the past, messages on this project have been sent by:
 1. Ordinary mail and face-to-face meetings
 2. Telephone calls
 3. Telex and telegrams
 4. There was really no way to fully satisfy this need.
How much money might be lost if a typical message does not reach the group members in a timely manner?
 1. Less than $1,000
 2. Between $1,000 and $5,000
 3. Between $5,000 and $15,000
 4. Over $15,000.
When you send a message, how many people need to see it?
 1. Less than 5
 2. 5 to 10 people
 3. Over 10 people.
Where are the other group members located?
 1. In the same building
 2. In the same city but in different buildings
 3. In different cities
 4. In different countries.
What is the nature of the issues your group discusses?
 1. General ideas, not related to decisions
 2. Policy and high-level issues
 3. Technical support decisions, technical management
 4. Operational decisions.
What is the purpose of the typical message?
 1. To keep others informed
 2. To request information
 3. To alert others to new developments
 4. To make specific assignments.
When you send a message, how important is the reply?
 1. Not important
 2. Nice to have
 3. It influences the outcome.
 4. It is vital to the project.
How do you feel about project information being "on record"?
 1. It would be better to keep most information private.
 2. Some information should be recorded to facilitate tracking.
 3. All information should be on record for better management.
What level of authority do you have to get a system installed?
 1. Someone else in another department makes that decision.
 2. Someone in my department will take my recommendation and will make the decision.
 3. Our project will make the decision with input from others.
 4. It's my decision.

After you complete the test, please add up the total number of points.
If your score is:

9 to 15 = You have no need for a message system.
16 to 21 = A message system would be nice to have, but you can do without one.
22 to 27 = Your organization would greatly benefit from a message system.
28 to 34 = You have an acute and immediate need for a message system.

Case Study 2: National Aeronautics and Space Administration (NASA)

This second case study illustrates usage patterns and group interaction in an organization with its own specific culture. NASA is a government agency and as such, its communications management needs differ from those of the nuclear community we used in the first case study.

NASA has actively used several computer conferencing systems since 1975 in support of three projects: the communications technology satellite, the Pacific Northwest Regional Commission, and the transportation system study.

1   The Communications Technology Satellite Project

Running a complex technological project among half a dozen government centers and about 20 contractors is a difficult task under any conditions. When project members are spread out over the entire United States, it is overwhelming. And when the project has to manage day after day a common resource situated 22,000 miles in outer space, the assignment leaves the realm of normal business and enters the domain of science fiction.

At NASA, one group of computer conferencing users conducted such a project under these exact conditions for more than 4 years. The resource they manage is the Communications Technology Satellite (CTS), a joint United States–Canada project. Among the government users are the Veterans Administration hospitals, the Goddard Space Flight Center, Lewis Research Center in Cleveland, Ohio, and Ames Research Center in California. Several universities and medical schools are also among the principal investigators, as well as commercial companies such as Satellite Business Systems, COMSAT, and Westinghouse. The group began using a system called PLANET in 1975, when the task of coordinating all the projects prior to the launch of the satellite became overwhelming.

Once the "bird" was in space, use of PLANET became routine: The project manager at NASA headquarters, Wasyl Lew, would enter his instructions into the system every morning and would monitor the progress of various projects and experiments. Each team would come in during the day at the most convenient time, receive the information it required, review group status, and broadcast its own requirements or notices if necessary.

Occasionally, a crisis would come up. For instance, when there was a power supply failure in 1976, priorities had to be met, responsibilities had to be allocated, and much negotiation was necessary. Most of this took place over PLANET. Because the transcripts of conferences were always retrievable, the CTS groups used PLANET as a running record for both day-to-day and long-term communication management.

Interviews of group leaders and a study of project transcripts showed that the group derived a number of benefits from the use of PLANET. These benefits were: the ability to integrate their communications into their own workday, provide greater precision of information, replace or support other media, and handle emergency situations. Users have also noted that access to PLANET extended their communications considerably, since less than half of their entries were made at a time when coast-to-coast phone conversation would have been practical because of time differences or conflicts in schedules.

NASA supported the storage costs for the whole effort, which amounted to an average of $167 per month. The software includes the ability to bill users individually even in the same project, which made it possible for contractors to support their own share of the coordination and management effort. A detailed cost analysis for the 14-month period ending in February 1979 was performed for presentation to NASA at the CTS project meeting held in Denver in April.

From such long-term usage it is possible to draw some precise estimates regarding the cost of operations of a large, ongoing project utilizing computer conferencing. Figure 2-10 shows the average PLANET invoice for each participating institution.

2   The Pacific Northwest Regional Commission

One of the most fruitful applications of computer conferencing is found in the management of planning projects, especially when federal and state government levels are involved. Use of PLANET by the Pacific Northwest (PNW) Regional Commission is a case in point. The commission was created in the spring of 1975

FIGURE 2-10   Average monthly costs for CTS groups.

AVERAGE MONTHLY COSTS FOR CTS GROUPS

$134 for Public Service Satellite Consortium
$107 for NASA (with an average of 12 participants)
$ 83 for the Joint Council on Educational Technology
$ 75 for the Lister Hill Medical Center of NIH
$ 73 for the Southern Educational Communications Assoc.
$ 69 for COMSAT, Inc.
$ 66 for the Veterans Administration
$ 59 for George Washington University
$ 58 for the University of Washington Medical School
$ 52 for the Federal Communications Commission
$ 46 for Satellite Business Systems, Inc.
$ 46 for Varian, Inc.
$ 45 for Stanford University
$ 44 for Westinghouse
$ 30 for the University of Illinois

by joint action of the governors of three northwestern states to evaluate the utility of LANDSAT data to provide land resource management information.

The members of the commission deal with policy decisions affecting land-use planning and the environment in the three states of Washington, Idaho, and Oregon. Their interaction may concern technical matters such as the data NASA supplies, or political and social matters such as setting priorities in response to the recent western drought.

To maintain close contact among the staffs of governors of these states, PLANET conferences were initiated in July 1977 by Dr. Dale Lumb of NASA. Participants in the conferences included not only those in the northwest states, but also resource persons at the NASA Ames Research Center in California. The discussions have concerned topics ranging from pending legislative actions to the quality of color images from space.

PLANET was used to set agendas for meetings, report their results, and schedule activities of the task force.

A review of the use of PLANET by the PNW group, based on statistics gathered by the system, shows the following: The group started relatively fast in the first month, then went through a period of increased organizational activity and system "learning," reaching a stable level of use during the last 3 months of 1977. Tabulation of the monthly volume of usage shows the cost stabilizing at $50 per month to connect one user with the rest of the group. Although the number of messages in each conference has tended to remain fairly constant, the average length of messages has become increasingly greater, approaching an average of about 100 words per public entry. This illustrates the learning process of a group which finds the appropriate level of usage as well as the appropriate types of content for which the PLANET system is suited.

FIGURE 2-11 Terminals were located in the offices of the governor's staff in three northwestern states. Other group members were in California.

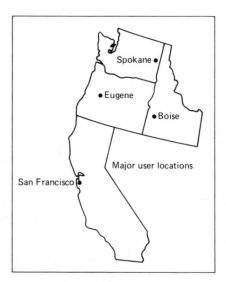

MONTH	WORDS DELIVERED	COST/15 WORDS
July 77	116,130	11 cents
August	52,581	22 cents
September	96,253	14 cents
October	21,172	36 cents
November	21,186	26 cents
December	25,617	26 cents
TOTAL	332,739	18 cents

FIGURE 2-12 Communications statistics summary.

The average cost of information delivery in PLANET is less than 25 cents per 15 words for this group (Fig. 2-12). As a comparison, at that time a telegram cost $4.75 for 15 words, plus $3.00 if printed and delivered. A Mailgram currently costs $2.75 per 100 words; a 5-minute telephone call from San Francisco to Boise costs $1.86. However, these cost comparisons do not tell the whole story. Avoiding the time delays inherent in mail and the inconvenience of scheduling telephone calls cannot be easily evaluated.

3 Future Transportation Systems

When the conference on "future transportation systems" began in September 1975, all the participants knew each other. They had worked together for about 6 months and had recognized a need for exchange of views among individuals working on the project. The study was jointly conducted by the Ames Office of Planning and Analysis and the Communications Branch to evaluate the concept of computer conferencing in an application involving an ongoing interagency–university–industry assessment of transportation technology.

The objective of the group was to make a series of recommendations concerning research and development for intercity air and ground transportation up to the year 2000. Before the computer conference the group met at a conference in Hershey, Pennsylvania, and began circulating drafts of various sections of the report. The purpose of the computer conference, then, was to promote the orderly assessment and integration of these documents while keeping face-to-face interaction to a minimum.

Once the conference was under way, communications among group members rose rapidly. The rate of private-message exchange was particularly high, prompted by the existence of two distinct subgroups (government and contractors). The charter under which the group was formed specified that each subgroup would exchange views among its own members in preparing drafts. This mandate encouraged the use of the private mode until integration in the public mode could take place. It also led to the creation of a new activity for the exclusive use of government personnel.

On November 19, 1975, the study group conducted a synchronous (real-time) management meeting over PLANET. On December 1, the final part of the conference (Part III) was created, and all subconferences which were still in the system were deleted.

Observations Regarding Media Usage

Figure 2-13 shows the distribution of entries by content category in both the transportation and CTS conferences. The percentage of entries in various categories may be compared for these two conferences. Learning and procedural entries are quite similar (9 percent and 8 percent for learning, 24 percent and 19 percent for procedural, respectively). The transportation study, however, involved a higher degree of social activity, which was the smallest of all categories for CTS.

With the completion of this project, NASA provided the first large-scale field test of computer conferencing in an operational setting. A review of the transcript provides a basis for several comments on media usage.

The major areas of application were found in the following activities:

Use of Message Systems to Replace or Supplement Other Media. Computer conferencing was often used to confirm and support information transmitted through other channels, as in this entry:

[458]   Hunczak   13-Feb-76   1:09 PM
The spacecraft was ranged by Goddard on February 10. Orbital elements were received

FIGURE 2-13   Content categories for two of the NASA conferences.

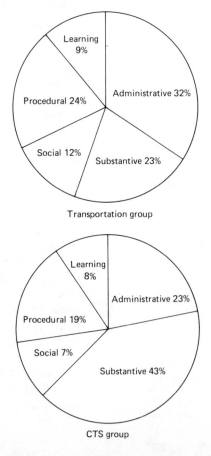

at Lewis this morning, processed, and the new S/Cephemeris and AZ-EL angles for your ground sites mailed this afternoon at 20 30, February 13. Would like to know when each receive them in the mail.

The author of this message needs confirmation that a certain document has been received through the mail. PLANET thus provided a record of the communications events taking place in the group.

Handling Emergency Situations   Instances of reliance on PLANET for crisis management among CTS projects and for decision making in urgent situations have been observed:

[521] Donoughe   4-Mar-76   8:06 AM
To all Pls and experimenters: a problem has developed with the spacecraft. The problem may be in the experiments power converter. All experiments are canceled until the problem is resolved. You will be updated as pertinent information becomes available.

Promoting an Effective Management Style   The following entry shows the use of the public mode to confirm private communications giving a number of participants a specific time allocation:

[516] Kennard   2-Mar-76   12:46 PM
Ippolito, Kaiser, Nunnally, Miller. Time allocations for the week of 3/7–3/13 follow by private message. Please let me know any corrections promptly.

Notice that the whole group is now informed that four experiments have been allocated time (although exact times are not made public). The two groups made effective use of the system in classical management tasks, such as communicating information, requesting data, giving assignments, and making sure deadlines were met. Such use is apparent in the following entry:

[317] Hall   28-Jan-76   9:33 AM
For the record, Mascy's questions of yesterday discussed by phone. Reports 2 and 8 and parts of 7 and 1 will be mailed in the next 3 days. As previously suspected, report 9 will be late (and won't reach Spaeth by next Wednesday). Berkeley or PMM will mail report 5 this week. To repeat: report 8 was never intended to be 'the' final report. See proposal, contract, and Admin. Report #2.

Extending Communications Beyond Working Hours   Figure 2-14 shows the distribution of conferencing sessions as a function of time of day. It can be seen that 36 percent of all sessions occurred outside west coast working hours. Of special significance to NASA is the expansion of the narrow "telephone window" between the east and west coasts. This greater flexibility in the use of time was noted by one participant in the transcript:

[173] Mascy   7-Jan-76   9:46 AM
. . . Just in passing. I noted the timeline of message 171 at 6:40 PM PST and message 172 at 5:25 AM PST . . . for what it is worth, the computer terminals have opened up the communications day to about 12 to 13 hours. . . . This might be compared to telephone day between East and West Coast of about 3 or 4 hours. . . .

Over 55 percent of all sessions took place outside the normal "telephone windows."

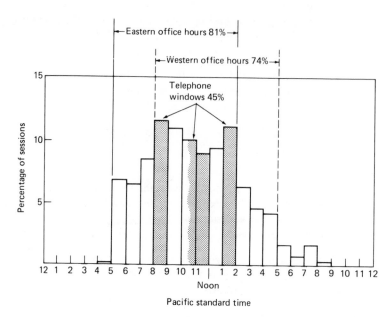

FIGURE 2-14   Distribution of sessions as a function of time of day.

Evaluation of User Attitudes

In computer conferencing, as with all other media, one needs to assume that the participants have mastered the basic skills required to use the system before any significant evaluation can take place. Most of the participants in the two conferences described here developed the required skills in a short time. The lack of typing skills did not prove to be a barrier, as was initially anticipated by some. Users developed definite opinions on the variety of tasks which they had to perform during the conferences. Among the tasks which were rated positively were: administrative activities; logistic and scheduling tasks; exchanges requiring short-term (but not immediate) response; very specific, narrowly defined issues; quantitative information transfer; and routine day-by-day communications. The ability to perform these tasks by leaving or retrieving messages at their convenience was, by far, the most important feature of the medium for them.

Users agreed that the use of this medium for synchronous conferencing (with more than two or three other people) headed the list of unsuitable uses. Tasks not well-suited to the medium included: substantive debates, especially when experts disagreed; broad issues; methods of getting to know each other; and situations which required immediate responses.

Users also agreed that computer conferencing replaced much telephone traffic. There was a general consensus that it reduced mail exchanges and saved some travel. However, PLANET was seen as more than a substitute for other media. With one exception, users believed that PLANET made a unique and beneficial contribution, which could not have been made by any other medium or combination of media, to the efforts of the group. Thus, computer conferencing was a supplement to existing communication modes as well as a substitute for certain kinds of communications.

In summary, the three most important values of the system were its time independence, the availability of hard copy, and the ability to enter one's message without interruption. Apart from the negative response to synchronous conferencing, user reactions ranged from satisfied to very enthusiastic. Use did not lead to mechanistic exchanges nor did respondents feel overwhelmed by information (although some felt burdened by irrelevant or trivial exchanges that they were forced to scan in order to extract information). Specific reactions to the system were similarly generally positive, notwithstanding the suggestions offered to make the system more responsive to the needs of these users.

THE ASSESSMENT OF COMMUNICATIONS NEEDS

New technologies bring with them new hopes that are often exaggerated. No matter how effective computer-based message systems might be, their benefits can only be realized within an organization that needs them. How to recognize and quantify that need is the subject of this chapter.

The assessment of communications needs attempts to answer two questions: First, can computer-based message systems support or replace existing communications patterns while reducing total cost and improving productivity? Second, are there special opportunities to be gained from the introduction of such a system?

THE INTERNAL COMMUNICATIONS AUDIT

There is no truly scientific way to measure the communications needs of an organization. The best we can do is describe it in qualitative terms, then "bracket" the total cost of communications by approaching that number from various directions.

It is a very rare company where management has a precise idea of its own communications cost. Telephone bills, of course, constitute a simple line item, but the expenses for Telex are often thrown into overhead. When it comes to letters, it may be possible to obtain reliable data, but if you ask about the number of meetings held or the purpose of specific trips, again the picture is very confused. The first approach to grasping the overall communications behavior of the organization is to conduct an internal audit.

Many sources describe techniques for this kind of assessment, taking it to a great degree of detail. For our purpose here a first approximation is all we require. We want to find out "where most of the money goes" and how much is actually available to be displaced—or saved—by new technology. An organization spending $10 a month on stamps and $25 in telephone bills probably does not have an urgent requirement for an electronic mail system. But another organization might spend thousands on mailings that do not require an ongoing dialogue with the recipient—therefore the sheet volume of communication does not tell the whole story. We not only need to know all the factors enumerated in the preceding chapter: the size of the organization, its number of branches, its favored management structure, and its culture, but also the actual division between communication directed inside the organization and that directed outside (the "internal fraction"). We will also need to evaluate the unit cost of each type of communication, a cost which may vary from one organization to another.

To conduct an internal communications audit, then, we will need access to various sources of data within the organization, typically starting with the controller, who will be in the best position to retrieve the total telephone amount and the total monthly bill for telegrams and Telexs. Both these categories will be broken down into domestic and international categories. The number of letters sent can be compiled from various sources, including the mail room. Again, the best approach will use multiple sources and will try to "bracket" the actual number in a realistic range instead of taking a single path and trying to hammer into place the last significant figure. The number of meetings per day can be estimated by walking around the organization, asking questions and observing general patterns. It is easy to spot areas that have been set aside as natural meeting places. More deceptive are the short "one-on-one meetings" which may not follow any pattern. (In the next section we will describe a different approach to this problem.) Formal meetings can be estimated more accurately by consulting the schedule for the use of conference rooms. Finally, the total number of trips is probably available through the office of the controller.

We will end up with a table like that shown in Fig. 3-1. This figure can be read as follows: What we have here is a fictitious financial organization, headquartered in New York City. It has a branch in London and one in Los Angeles, and employs 25 people in all, working 20 days a month. Each person makes an average of seven phone calls a day, six of them within the country. Each person also sends one letter and one telegram or Telex and initiates three meetings with another person. We assume that the one-on-one meetings last about 5 minutes for a total cost of 10 minutes at $30 per professional hour, or $5.80. In 1 month there are 30 group meetings with average attendances of four people, lasting 1 hour each time; the unit cost of the average group meeting is thus set, conservatively, at $120.

Knowing what percentage of each category of communications is internal, we can compute the total volume—hence, the total cost of communication that could be transferred to various kinds of message systems. In the case of the organization in question the audit leads us to estimate that about $17,000, or roughly a third of its monthly communications cost, could be affected by a new technology. This, of course, does not mean that this amount would necessarily be *saved*, since the replacement technology would have its own operating costs.

Although a communications audit sounds like a simple, rational operation, it represents a task of considerable magnitude if the organization has developed any degree of bureaucracy. Many attempts to introduce electronic mail into companies

FIGURE 3-1   Internal communications audit (example).

COMMUNICATION TYPE	UNITS PER PERSON PER DAY	TOTAL MONTHLY NUMBER	UNIT COST	TOTAL MONTHLY COST	INTERNAL FRACTION	AMOUNT THAT CAN BE SAVED
Letters	1	500	$8	$4,000	50%	$2,000
Domestic TELEX and telegrams	0.5	250	$10	$2,500	50%	$1,250
International TELEX & Telegr.	0.5	250	$30	$7,500	50%	$3,750
Domestic phone calls	6	3000	$3	$9,000	20%	$1,800
International phone calls	1	500	$25	$12,500	10%	$1,250
One-on-one meetings	3	1500	$5	$7,500	50%	$3,750
Group meetings		30	$120	$3,600	60%	$2,150
Trips		8	$700	$5,600	25%	$1,400
				$52,200		$17,350 (33%)

that were obviously wasting fortunes on Telex and the telephone have been foiled by the simple fact that such fortunes were spent in overhead items of the organization's budget, where a particular project leader or division manager received neither praise nor blame for a contribution to the total. When the electronic mail facility was entered as a special line item called "timesharing service" or as "data processing" within the budget of the individual project or division, it became clearly visible to management, and an easy target for misplaced cost-cutting.

COMMUNICATIONS COSTS AND TIME PRODUCTIVITY

The internal communications audit gives us only a first approximation of the impact a new technology might have. It will probably work well for a small organization like the financial company mentioned in the example. However, such an audit does not show the actual displacement in terms of the time that various professionals spend communicating. Ignoring this factor has made many fine studies invalid in the view of management. Suppose a letter costs $8.00 by the time it is mailed, and suppose the same message could be sent electronically for 50 cents. The apparent savings are $7.50. But if sending it electronically requires the attention of an expert, or if the author is now given a terminal to send his or her own messages, what we have really done is to invest $7.50 of the organization's money into an effort to transform every manager into a secretary. We have made the secretaries miserable and the managers inefficient. We have squandered much more than $7.50 per letter in an attempt to manipulate costs that were basically dissimilar because they represented different *functions* within the organization.

One approach to this new problem consists in refining the results of the communications audit by selecting a pilot group of about 20 people to serve as the standard for the construction of the typical workday. Managers, professionals, and clerical personnel should be represented within this pilot group. Each member of the group is given a logbook and a timer. The timer is set to go off either at random times or at regular intervals (for instance, every 20 minutes). The participant is asked to record in the logbook his or her activity at the time of the signal. The logbook also records every meeting and telephone call. Secretaries are asked to record the calls they receive and the mail they type.

Once the samples from the pilot group have been recorded, it is possible to obtain a fairly accurate picture of the organization's communications behavior, and to compare it with that of other groups (Fig. 3-2). Projected savings can then be established. Participants are interviewed in depth at the end of the study.

In one such study (which is thought to be typical of an industrial organization in the United States), it was found that participants in the pilot group spent 35 percent of their time in meetings. They indicated that 25 percent of the meetings were too long and 23 percent were nonproductive. Ten percent of their time was spent on the phone, and half these calls were placed to transmit information one way—in other words, they could have been replaced by either a text message or a voice message.

In addition, various studies report that between 40 percent and 70 percent of

FIGURE 3-2   The first step in the analysis of time productivity is to establish how a typical pilot group of about 20 managers, professionals, and clerical personnel are spending their working time.

phone calls do not reach the intended party the first time. Other categories in the use of time were: writing, searching, or compiling information, and traveling, each of which activity occupied about 10 percent of the time (4).

To evaluate potential savings, we then analyze the time spent in each activity to estimate what fraction can be transferred to a computer-based message system (Fig. 3-3). In the case of one-on-one meetings savings can amount to as much as 50 percent. Such meetings are usually limited to a simple exchange of information that did not require interruption of the participants' activity. Travel may be eliminated in as much as one-quarter of all cases if computer conferencing is used, and about one-quarter of all telephone calls can also be substituted.

These figures, again, are only gross approximations of what we find in a large

FIGURE 3-3   The second step in our analysis of time productivity will be to find out what percentage of each category of communications can be taken over by a computer-based message system.

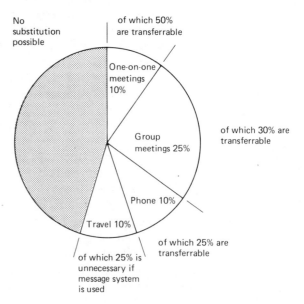

One-on-one meeting		Electronic mail	
Speaker		Sender	
Get up/Walk/Speak/Return	3 minutes	Initiate	.15 minute
Recovery	2 minutes	Type average message	.45 minute
	5 minutes	Send	.15 minute
		Recovery	.75 minute
Listener			2.50 minute
Listen/Speak	2 minutes	Receiver	
Recovery	1 minute	Initiate	.15 minute
	3 minutes	Read	.15 minute
		File	.25 minute
		Recovery	.30 minute
			1.40 minute
TOTAL _____	8 minutes	TOTAL _____	3.90 minutes

FIGURE 3-4   In this analysis of short face-to-face meetings in one industrial organization, it was found that the use of electronic mail could have 50 percent efficiency.

company. Specific numbers depend on the area of business, the size, the degree of centralization, and the management structure of each organization.

Knowing the distribution of time among the various categories was step 1 (Fig. 3-2). Estimating the fraction that could be transferred to a computer-based message system was step 2 (Fig. 3-3). To complete the analysis we now need to compute the efficiency of this substitution for every communication category. The results obtained in one such analysis are shown in Figs. 3-4 to 3-6 for one-on-one meetings, group meetings, and telephone calls, respectively. For example, an electronic mail system may eliminate the need to play "telephone tag" and disrupt the activities of other people, but it does require some time to initiate, compose, send, and file the message. Each organization should do its own analysis of efficiency, because the results will be affected by its business, culture, structure, and the tools at its disposal. The study may show that the substitution of electronic mail for phone calls was only 50 percent efficient.

FIGURE 3-5   This study of computer conferencing showed approximately 30 percent efficiency gain over face-to-face meetings that could be substituted. (*Credit: S. Costello, private communication*)

Four-person face-to-face meeting		Four-person face-to-face conference	
Travel	5 minutes	Travel	0 minute
Shoulder time	12 minutes (waiting)	Shoulder time	0 minute
Discussion	33 minutes	Reading	16 minutes
Travel & recovery	10 minutes	Thinking	8 minutes
		Dictating	8 minutes
	60 minutes per person		32 minutes (dictating) or 48 minutes if typing

Average phone call	Electronic messaging	
15 minutes for two persons	Initiate	0.15 minute
	Dictate 180 words	1.50 minutes
	Read 180 words	1.00 minute
	File	0.25 minute
	TOTAL	3.90 minutes/ person or 7.80 minutes for two persons.

FIGURE 3-6   Electronic messaging may result in almost 50 percent efficiency over the average telephone call when the purpose of the communications is purely information exchange. (*S. Costello, private communication*)

Once these efficiency estimates are obtained, we can complete the third step and calculate the total expected gain. Using the numbers found in our example so far (Fig. 3-7), we would conclude there would be a potential gain of 8.5 percent for the managers, professionals, and clerical personnel in that company. For a branch of a modern organization employing 100 managers, professionals, and office workers, this figure could easily translate into savings of a million dollars a year.

Exciting as they are, the results of such a study must be approached with caution. At every step we have made assumptions that could be critically challenged. For example, how do we know that the pilot group is representative of company

FIGURE 3-7   The third step in the analysis of the impact of computer-based message systems is to compute the total saving. In this fictitious (but typical) industrial organization, the system can save over 8 percent of total office personnel time.

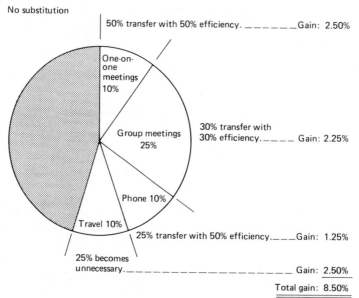

No substitution

50% transfer with 50% efficiency. _ _ _ _ _ _ Gain: 2.50%

One-on-one meetings 10%

Group meetings 25%

30% transfer with 30% efficiency. _ _ _ _ Gain: 2.25%

Phone 10%

Travel 10%

25% transfer with 50% efficiency. _ _ _ Gain: 1.25%

25% becomes unnecessary. _ _ _ _ _ _ _ _ _ _ _ _ _ _ _ _ _ _ Gain: 2.50%

Total gain: 8.50%

personnel? How do we know the distribution of time among various categories was accurately measured? More importantly, can we be sure that the fraction of communication we regard as transferrable was not really masking other forms of interaction and social contact? There is more to management than passing messages around, and the rest of this book will show that the transfer of communications activity is not a simple translation across media. It requires an adaptation of organization structures and a great deal of skill on the part of users.

In a detailed study of office communications for a large military installation with 3000 employees, office automation consultant Addie Mattox has introduced a variant of the previous approach. The organization worked on 300 long-term projects, had a low ratio of secretaries to professionals, a matrix approach to staffing, and significant distance between buildings—as much as 35 miles. The study was more extensive than the previous one. It consisted of two phases: a pilot group of 30 people in one technical department, followed by interviews with about 250 people from other departments (5).

The methodology also included "shadowing" of group members and a detailed analysis of information flow. The results are shown in Fig. 3-8.

In practice, benefits from the use of the automated system (in this case, a network of Xerox STAR workstations) developed fairly slowly. There were not enough terminals to make electronic mail effective, so that users had to send information electronically to some people, by ordinary mail to other. Another complaint was the slowness and unreliability of the software. "As time passes," notes Mattox, "users have become increasingly comfortable with electronic mail, and its usage is rising each month."

As this last experience indicates, any new system must be analyzed in its context. To say that electronic mail can replace telephone calls is similar to saying that a surgeon can remove a person's heart and replace it with a donor's heart. The technical difficulty of the substitution is only the beginning of the problem. The real scientific challenge comes with an understanding of the mechanism of rejection and with the control of the phenomena that surround it. We will return to this analogy later when we discuss the specific challenges of electronic mail. For the moment it is enough to pose questions about the accuracy of our time productivity estimates.

What we hope we have accomplished in this analysis is the convergence of various sets of numbers that will "bracket" the total communications budget of the

FIGURE 3-8   Potential time savings resulting from the automation of office communications. (*Credit: A. Mattox.*)

Activity	Potential Time Saving By:		
	Managers	Technical	Support
Telephone	6%	5%	8%
Informal meetings	7%	6%	3%
Formal meetings	2%	2%	5%
Mail	1%	1%	2%
Travel	3%	5%	3%
TOTAL	19%	19%	21%

organization. The internal audit, on one hand, and the time productivity study, on the other, give us an overall estimate of the amount of money that *could* be saved if advanced message technology were employed. Together, these two approaches may also reveal some areas where communication patterns can be drastically improved although nothing in the numbers made the fact obvious. And the greatest benefits may lie in those areas.

HIDDEN BENEFITS

The problem with the kind of analysis we have reviewed above is that it addresses only what can be measured. It is a basic shortcoming of quantitative research. You cannot compute the future sales of Xerox machines from measuring the consumption of carbon paper, and you cannot project the *real* need for message systems from the number of letters and phone calls alone. In many organizations communications flow along lines established by tradition. To simply automate this flow may save some money, but it does not address the really vital concerns of management: how to improve survival, how to increase competitiveness, how to improve decisions. And it is at that vital level that computer-based message systems can be most effective.

At the other end of the spectrum we find those organizations that are doing surprisingly well *without* the benefit of advanced forms of communication. Either they do not really have a need to communicate, or their need is so specialized that it cannot be satisfied by a message system. Some businesses are not geared to a community of stable customers but to a constantly changing parade of participants. They may have a high communications bill but they are not candidates for automation. Other businesses may have an intense need for communications, but each interaction is so brief that the *context* of the conversation becomes the medium itself. The trading floor of a major financial institution is an example of that extreme state of information overload where deals are made simply by gesture or by voice in the middle of thousands of messages that are often exchanged at a subliminal level. In that environment there is a place for a computer message system but the demands on it in terms of access speed and presentation of the data make it quite unique.

We also find organizations where no interaction is taking place among certain units simply because no tool has ever been available to support that interaction. This is a type of need that no amount of analysis will bring out. An internal audit will reveal only the absence of communications and the time productivity study will be completely misleading.

An example of such an organization is an engineering firm working on large, remote projects. Because there has not been a convenient form of contact with remote sites (such as mining projects in Africa or drilling operations in Asia), the structure of such organizations has adapted to a management style where day-to-day reporting to headquarters is minimized. An executive culture has evolved where most important decisions can be made on-site, and where information follows later as formal reports.

Such an organization can be revolutionized by the introduction of a message system, yet its impact falls entirely outside the classical analysis in terms of "office automation." The advent of international networks, microwave technology for links to the site itself, and the availability of portable terminals or even rugged personal computers, make possible an entirely new pattern of management. In this new pattern communications costs will increase drastically (they were nonexistent before), and this will no doubt cause some distress to the accountants if no budget category is available to handle the new activity. But these increases will be offset by extraordinary gains in the efficiency of the whole organization.

In the study mentioned previously, Mattox (5) reports a significant conclusion:

> The time savings . . . come from quantifiable activities. However, there are important unquantifiable benefits as well.

Among these "hidden benefits" she finds better decisions (based on more current information), the ability to react faster to changes, increased convenience of setting up meetings, and improved collaboration among team members.

In summary: The assessment of communications needs invites us to measure what can be measured, but we look at the results with caution. We try to combine various approaches to bracket our estimate of the actual savings. Our goal is to answer the question: "Is there sufficient potential for substitution among the existing forms of communications to warrant the introduction of a computer-based message system?" As we examine the elements of the answer we remain alert for the hidden benefits which may arise when the new technology makes possible a form of group interaction that has never been available before.

Case Study 3: Petroleum Applications

Our third case study concerns an oil company engaged in major exploration projects around the world. Its headquarters are in Tulsa and it has offices in Houston. Within the company, the Energy Resource Group that pioneered in the use of electronic messaging and computer conferencing to support drilling activities is in Manila. Engineers and geologists in Manila, Houston, and Tulsa continued active discussions through use of the NOTEPAD conferencing system. After over 1 year of usage the office automation group performed a detailed review of the patterns of communications that resulted from use of the system, and they interviewed the principal participants.

The study found that the computer conference had been used to displace teletype messages and phone calls between Houston, Tulsa, and Manila. Approximately 255 messages had been sent per month, each message about 120 words long.

The state of communications prior to the introduction of the system was summarized as follows:

> Before NOTEPAD, the teletype and telephone were the main vehicles of communication. The average teletype costs $7 to send, the average call to Manila cost $100. Telephone calls required time at night to communicate with Manila since there is a 14-hour time difference. These calls often interfere with family life.

A definite impact was measured on time productivity. Secretaries reported that the system saved them about 1½ hours on the phone per week, or about $400 per month.

The impact on the working patterns of these individuals was felt in other ways, which the report summarizes as follows:

All the participants said that convenience of use was their prime motivating factor in using NOTEPAD. They felt NOTEPAD *increased their ability to exchange information*. Unlike the telephone, all public messages sent were available to all participants. Since all are privy to most of the discussions, messages between Manila and Tulsa do not have to be relayed to the project manager in Houston. Most individuals also had terminals at home where they would check on events during the night hours before bedtime and on the weekends. This allowed them to respond to any situations easily and quickly. NOTEPAD eliminated the long phone calls that they often received at their homes at night.

It was interesting to observe how use of the system grew from its early introduction (as an office automation experiment) to its active use on a major drilling operation:

All the participants interviewed said they had a rather weak interest in beginning the NOTEPAD conference, but after a year's use their interest in the project has become very strong because of the convenience of NOTEPAD and the ability to communicate easily over time and distance.

All the participants began by typing in their own messages, but after a few months they delegated this task to their secretary. Each morning the secretaries list the messages sent to each principal, the principals read the messages when it is convenient, and either dictate or transcribe notes to secretaries for them to send.

The major benefits of the use of the system, however, came as unforeseen byproducts of the "overt" applications. The project manager estimated that between $50,000 and $100,000 was saved per year in capital expenditures thorugh the use of the system. It became possible for the management offices in Houston to monitor requests for equipment sent by operations in Manila to engineering in Tulsa. It became possible to recognize, for instance, where a spare piece of equipment could be located or borrowed from another project without shipping another one all the way to the Philippines. The increased access to communications, and the ability to engage in conferencing were the primary cause of the capital cost avoidance.

Charges for the use of the system were $5,500 per month. These rates were subsequently reduced through the use of word processing equipment to construct messages offline, and then send them into the system at high speed.

This study, based on the use of a computer conferencing system for over a year in a large industry setting, shows all three of the impacts mentioned in the previous chapter: hard dollar savings, time productivity gains, and very significant hidden benefits.

## PART TWO

# TWO

TOOLS OF
MESSAGE SYSTEMS

CHAPTER **4**

TOOLS OF
ELECTRONIC MAIL

FROM TERMINAL LINKS TO NETWORK MAIL: THE EXAMPLE OF ARPANET AND PLATO

In this section we begin the study of the software tools used in message systems by looking at their evolution on two large computer networks of considerable sophistication.

The terms "electronic mail" or "computer mail" are used to describe the use of a computer-based message system to compose, edit, send, and file person-to-person messages. In many networks the simplest version of such message exchange takes the form of real-time links between two terminals. Linking one terminal with another effectively transforms the devices into teletype machines, with the computer simply serving as a switch. Every character typed on terminal A appears instantly on terminal B.

The immediacy of this mode of communication seems to be a strong positive point for some users, especially programmers who need fast response on technical problems from colleagues on the same computer. It is also considered a negative feature by others because of the interruption it causes in ongoing work, the psychological pressure of watching every keystroke, hesitation, or mistake transmitted without a chance to edit, and the social awkwardness of refusing links.

For these reasons the two tasks under which links are most effective are training and debugging. Figure 4-1 shows one example of LINK.

On the Advanced Research Projects Agency (ARPA) network, a more sophisticated form of electronic message exchange appeared in the early 1970s. It began as "SEND MESSAGE" and evolved into a full-scale network mail facility which let any user of any ARPANET computer send a message to any other. This demanded a central directory and common message protocols and standards for all sites, since the network linked machines of various sizes and manufacture.

The SEND MESSAGE facility, whose actual use is illustrated in Fig. 4-2, rapidly became the most popular feature of ARPANET and was heavily applied. In fact, it was so successful that network users later refused to consider other, more advanced forms of computer communication when they became available.

FIGURE 4-1   The ARPANET LINK facility.

```
To link to the user at TTY7:
@ link SP 7 CR
LINK FROM ICCC, TTY 103
@ ;hello ray. CR          Messages over "link" should be preceded by semi-colon.
@;HELLO, WHO IS IT?   Questions and comments from TTY?.
@ ;this is abhay bhushan from mit, can you help me?   CR
@;OF COURSE, HOW ARE YOU ABHAY?
@ ...............          Conversation continues.
@ ;nice talking to you.  bye.   CR
@ break CR                Break the "link", please.
```

```
To send a message to another user:
@ sndmsg CR
TYPE LIST OF USERS: iccc CR     SNDMSG is self explanatory.
TYPE MESSAGE. EDIT WITH CONTROL-A, Q, R, X END WITH CONTROL-Z.
INSERT A FILE WITH CONTROL-B.
hello, this is a test. CR
↑Z
    End message with control-Z


To print a message:
@ typ ESC  E (FILE) message.tx ESC  T;1 CR    ESCAPE (i.e., altmode, denoted
                                               ESC causes completion of TYPE
                                               command and filename MESSAGE.
                                               TXT;1.
; (ICCC)MESSAGE.TXT;1    SAT 2-SEP-72 4:42PM   PAGE 1
2-SEP-72 1642 ICCC
HELLO, THIS IS A TEST MESSAGE.
```

FIGURE 4-2 The SEND MESSAGE facility. (*Reprinted from "ARPANET Scenarios," a set of demonstrations given at ICCC, 1972.*)

In systems like SEND MESSAGE and its successors, such as HERMES, ONTYME, and COMET, there is no provision for immediate response. A message is sent into a mailbox for later access by the recipient. No automatic filing is provided: Any searching of message files requires users to write their own search programs, and to flag those messages they want to retain or erase. The burden is placed on users to manage their own files, and a fairly detailed understanding of programming and file structures is required. Both senders and receivers must learn about 20 commands, and if they misuse them they can jeopardize the entire data structure. Some messages may even be lost in the process. These drawbacks are compensated for by the fact that the cost per message is very low.

Electronic mail systems have also evolved on systems designed to support education, training, or computer-assisted instruction, such as PLATO. The concept of PLATO evolved from research conducted at the University of Illinois and at Control Data Corporation. The research included the development of advanced terminals and special languages for the author of computer-assisted courseware.

The need for a communications link among PLATO terminals emerged very early in support of courseware development and in remote user training. Most communications functions were not anticipated in the basic design of PLATO. Instead, subsequent features evolved organically in response to the needs of a particular group of programmers at a particular time.

All PLATO software is aimed at creating, executing, and monitoring lessons. Lessons are written in the TUTOR language and can be linked in various ways by the teachers. They are executed by students in real time without access to the TUTOR level. There is no communication capability in the student mode, unless dialogue is initiated by the instructor. Students have no access to the system functions that initiate communication.

In the author mode, two types of information exchange features have evolved. In this respect, PLATO is following the pattern of development that appeared early on ARPANET with the LINK facility and the SEND MESSAGE facility. In synchronous exchange (real time), there are two systems for simultaneous interaction. In asynchronous (delayed) interaction, the systems available include capabilities called *Note*, *Memo*, and *Journal*. These features appear to have been created to satisfy short-term needs, but they may be called upon to serve a permanent role.

The PLATO equivalent of the LINK facility is called TALK. One terminal establishes a link with another, and a "master/slave" relationship can even be created in what is called "monitor mode." TALK messages are limited to a single line, but both users can type at the same time. What they type is written character by character at the bottom of the screen. In monitor mode, the rest of the screen can be shared between master and slave (but not in the other direction). Generally, this is used by an instructor viewing work of a student who has difficulty with a lesson.

The advantages of this form of communications are obvious in training and in demonstrations. The system is also useful in joint writing projects and curriculum development, and is extensively used in software development.

Disadvantages are also clear: Communications can exist only among users who are on the system at the same time and are not busy with something else. It is not reviewable or retrievable. It is restricted to a single line. It enables only two people to exchange ideas.

Another communication program lets up to five users communicate in real time. This process evolved around a TUTOR lesson that handles six channels with up to five users in each. The channel represents a common discussion area that can be opened, protected, or locked. In the locked mode, users vote to decide whether or not to admit newcomers. Information is typed character by character on several lines.

Several systems also allow asynchronous communication among PLATO users in typical electronic mail fashion. They include facilities for group notes, memos, and a journal, the latter being a repository for long comments that can be discussed in short form via notes.

The notes and memo systems are very similar to the ARPANET message system, with coordinators setting up access modes to define who gets in and at what level. This kind of capability is quite useful, as it enables disseminated participants to stay in touch. In the most commonly used system, known as "Group-Notes," there are several classes of users and provision for a director role. A user can either respond to a note or create a new one. On the negative side, the system does not allow review of entries except in serial fashion. New messages generally cannot be sorted, filed, or ignored, although a sophisticated user can "transport" various kinds of notes through buffers. There is no data search capability in the Group-Notes context, and the system cannot provide a list of all the Group-Notes. Nor can it apply to them any facility to search for key words, to save information, or to recombine information. This implies a self-limiting feature—if the system were ever used heavily, users would spend all their time managing the flow of information. Clearly, this approach calls for powerful file management functions that had not yet appeared at the time of our survey of the system.

PLATO is deceptively easy to use and promotes undisciplined growth of new message-handling software. A similar situation has been developing on ARPA-NET, with over five systems in current use for electronic mail. Indeed, Myer and Dodds have observed that "a surprising aspect of the message service is the unplanned, unanticipated, and unsupported nature of its birth and early growth"(6).

The key to the design of communications-oriented software is the careful study of the needs of the end user, followed by detailed analysis of actual usage patterns once the system is in the field. The lesson structure in PLATO is superb and reflects a thorough study of the academic environment for which it was intended. No similar study has been conducted for communications features, however. None of the dialogue systems in current use on PLATO seem to have been designed with a specific user population in mind, and no statistics are available regarding their performance. Once implemented, various features have tended to spread to other areas until they now overlap one another. This situation is confusing to the novice user and can become a source of frustration to the experienced one. User communities evolve as they grow in size and mix of interests. These changing usage patterns must be carefully observed to guide the evolution of system features.

It seems difficult to forecast what the solution will be for the proliferation of message software on education-oriented systems. The communications profile of each user is course-dependent, and this diversity does not help in designing a uniform approach to the software. The TALK facility is clearly needed to satisfy the needs of development, training, and demonstrations. From a systems viewpoint, all the other functions do not form a single, streamlined medium supporting communication. And from a user viewpoint, they have severe shortcomings.

There is much to learn from the natural evolution of these systems. ARPANET and PLATO represent the two earliest communities of sophisticated network users in America. Communications among them evolved to solve a social need, not a business need. Their powers and drawbacks may define the features of current and future systems.

ELECTRONIC MAIL FUNCTIONS IN BUSINESS SYSTEMS: COMET AND ON-TYME

At this point in our study of electronic mail it will be useful to review rapidly the features of two systems that have enjoyed wide attention; namely, the COMET system and ON-TYME, the network-wide system developed by TYMNET. They illustrate two approaches to the problem of providing message functions to business users equipped with ordinary terminals and desiring an inexpensive replacement for Telex.

The COMET System

COMET is a system offered by the Computer Corporation of America (CCA). It can be used on a service basis to send messages to other subscribers, or it can be purchased for internal use on certain computers. Every user of COMET is known by name and is assigned a mailbox, and the service charge is based in part on the number of mailboxes used by a client organization.

When the user has logged in, COMET brings him or her up to date with the number of new messages waiting, and it expects a command to be typed at the terminal. Available commands are:

COMPOSE	ANSWER	FORWARD
SEND	DELETE	HELP
READ	DISPLAY	SET
RETRIEVE	EDIT	LOGOUT
SCAN	FILE	

Before sending a message the user must compose it.

```
Command: COMPOSE
To: Jim Thorpe
cc: Kate Califano
Subject: New Sales Handbook
Text:
Kate is revising the report. Did you give her your reactions to the first draft?
.
Command: SEND
CCA 12-FEB-79 12:06:50 460 1
Message sent.
```

The end of the message is signaled by a period. COMET then files the message in the unsent file until you are ready to send it.

Other functions connected with message sending are:

```
FILE IN THORPE (which would let you save the message you just sent in your own
        THORPE file)
EDIT (which would let you replace a header, add a name to the carbon copy list, or
        edit the text)
READ (which would give you back the edited text for checking before you actually
        send it)
```

The user can also send a message answering a previous one, by using a facility described below.

Assume that you have just logged in to the COMET system, and it has told you:

```
Please type your name: Bill Smith
Password:
Thank you. Your last login was Thursday, Feb 8, 1979
11:40:59. You have 3 new messages.
```

You could now access your messages in the following way:

```
Command: READ
To: Bill Smith
From: Andrea Bergson
Date: FRI 9-FEB-79 11:51:52 EST
Subject: Sales Meeting
— — — — — — — — — — — —

Are you going to the sales meeting?

— — — — — — — — — — — —
```

You can also scan your unread messages:

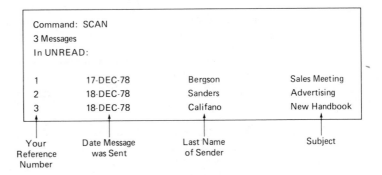

The SCAN command enables you to look at other files you have created, including both messages you have received and those you have sent.

You can read messages by number and you can also perform such requests as:

```
READ 1-3
READ ALL
READ 3,2
READ 2,REST
```

To answer a message you have just read you can specify that the answer will go only to the sender, or to all people who have received it. The system will then prompt you for the text and will give you an opportunity to read and send your response. It will create a "Re:" field containing the subject of the received message, name of sender, date, and time of that message, and its identification.

Just as you can answer a message, you can forward to other users one or more of the messages you have received, including your own comments along with the forwarded messages.

Note that the burden is on each user to create files of the messages to be retained for future use. These files can be scanned (along with the unsent and unread files).

Messages from unsent files can be sent in any order (or the user can use the command: SEND ALL).

The FILE function allows you to manipulate information in ways such as the following:

```
Command: FILE 1,3 in BROCHURE
You don't have a BROCHURE file.
Do you wish to create one? (Y or N): N

Command: FILE 1,3 in MARKETING
```

Messages and entire files can be deleted or retrieved. The RETRIEVE command lets the user look for a specific ID or a particular name or value in fields labeled *To*, *cc*, *From*, *Date*, and *Subject*. Some text editing functions are also provided to help the user compose text. The DISPLAY command provides:

A list of your files

A list of all subscribers and distribution lists

A summary of statistical information about your usage of the system, such as number of logins, messages, addresses, connect hours, messages stored, and files created since a given date

The SET command lets the user change password, page length, CRT mode, or format of message text.

The ON-TYME System

In an approach that differs radically from that of COMET, every user of ON-TYME is known by an identifier composed of an account code followed by a station code and separated by a period, such as:

AMEX.NY or SYBEX.ZAKS

ON-TYME is an electronic mail service offered by TYMNET, Inc., a California-based company, which operates an international computer network. ON-TYME became operational in August 1977. It runs on a Honeywell Level 6 computer, and another version has been developed for the DEC System 10 computer. The average cost of a message is said to be in the 30- to 40-cent range (at this writing). A full page of text (4000 characters) can be sent to two recipients for about $1.25 per copy from cities where there are local nodes (this assumes no extensive editing). The same text sent to five recipients counts as five messages.*

Each ON-TYME user has a workspace of approximately 15 single-spaced pages.

*From the article "ON-TYME—A Computer Message System," by Walter Ulrich (no reference given). These figures are naturally subject to change, and are quoted here only to provide an order of magnitude.

The user types the text into this workspace. Then it can be sent in several ways. Within the sender's account the message can be sent with a simple name:

SEND MKTG

The system responds with:

ACCEPTED AS #219470

Outside of the sender's account the command will include the account code and the station code; for instance:

SEND HARRY.NY

The same message can be sent to more than one user simply by stringing their names together. (To get a confirmation copy just add your own name to the list.)

Another way to send a message to several users is to give a group code. Groups in ON-TYME can have up to 255 members. Group codes begin with asterisks, and you must repeat the SEND command for each group:

```
SEND **VP
ACCEPTED AS #219522
SEND **ACCT
ACCEPTED AS #219523
```

Messages can also be sent to the "mailroom" station which is attached to every account by typing:

SEND-MAIL

Users can also add "carbon copy" lists to a message; they can append notes such as RUSH or INFO to indicate its urgency. After a message is sent, the user can append new text to it by typing: MORE, and the additional information.

To check a message after it is prepared and before it is sent the user can display the text on the terminal by using the command TYPE.

To reuse a message after it is sent you can bring it back into your workspace:

```
GET 220710
ACCEPTED
SEND LA
ACCEPTED AS #222662
```

Note that each sender has an "out list" showing each message that has been sent to, but not yet read by, a recipient. When a message is read, it is removed from the list. To have the list printed, the user types OUT and is shown a table like the following:

NAME	SENT	DATE	MSG #
MKTG	16:48	12 DEC 77	222967
KT–DVS	16:53	12 DEC 77	222969
AMEX–NY	16:53	12 DEC 77	222969
MAIL	16:59	12 DEC 77	222970

Recipient's ID Sender's Local Time Acceptance Number

The GET command can also be used to recall text files already prepared and stored within the system. These files can be renamed and cleared at will.

ON-TYME keeps an "in list" for each recipient. It shows all messages sent to you that you have not yet read. The IN command will print this list. The messages are then listed as follows:

SENDER	SEND	DAY	LENGTH	MSG #	
SF	10:16	2	54	223686	
MKTG	10:42	2	93	223692	RUSH
KI–DVS	13:25	2	160	223704	INFO
BRK–H.LA	13:49	2	78	223713	

Sender's ID   Your   Day
or Station   Local   of
Code   Time   Month

The commands to read the messages are:

```
READ
READ-ALL
READ 223692
```

You will then receive the message text, which appears as follows:

```
:READ 223692⤸

PT-GRN 197 11:29 2DEC77
CHRIS MARTIN
WE WILL USE SILVER EAGLE BUS LINES AGAIN THIS YEAR FOR THE WEST
COAST TOURS. ALTHOUGH THE LINE LOST A BUSLOAD OF OUR TOURISTS
IN BLACK DOG FOREST FOR A FEW HOURS LAST SUMMER, THEY HAVE AN
OTHERWISE EXCELLENT RECORD OF CUSTOMER SERVICE AND
SATISFACTION. —TERRY
ARROYO
CC TO:EV-GLBG LS-GSKY KT-DVS CONTR
NY 223715 10:15 2DEC77
```

Note that the heading contains a message sequence number (197). This differs from the message acceptance number, which is 223692. Each ID has its own sequence numbers, assigned as the messages sent to that ID are read.

An effort to be exhaustive about such services cannot be made here. Electronic mail systems come and go and evolve rapidly. Some are based on word processing machines, such as the Wang units. Others are adjuncts to database consultation services such as the Source and Compuserve. New generations of these services are emerging now on personal computers. All share most of the functions seen in the two examples above, from sending and reading to simple filing and editing. They also share their limitations: The systems demand a fairly high level of skill from their users, and they place the burden of file management squarely on users' shoulders. For example, a group of users can define itself as a "distribution list," but there is no provision for the dynamic management of these lists or for a system of human "roles" and related privileges reflecting group leadership and structure. Future systems will include such functions as a critical part of their design.

USER ROLES IN AN ADVANCED SYSTEM: JENNY

The JENNY system, which is a product of Infomedia, runs on HP-3000 computers. The fundamental concept in the design of JENNY is that a successful computer message system is much more than a "store-and-forward" program. To develop such a system strictly as an inexpensive alternative to Telex is insufficient. The major problem with earlier forms of communications was not cost, but lack of convenience in filing and retrieval. *A communications system should be an information resource in time and space, not simply a wire through which volatile messages can travel from point A to point B.*

Computer mail systems can be used not only to make such messages travel to more places but also to retain them; file them for the convenience of each user; make them available to programs, databases, and text editors; and anticipate their retrieval under a wide variety of search criteria.

JENNY is an electronic mail system designed with exactly these capabilities in mind. It uses nine fundamental commands that are each reduced to a single keystroke. And it recognizes the need for every user organization to control message distribution lists and to provide centralized maintenance of key words.

The *message* is the key concept in JENNY. Most interaction between users of JENNY is in the form of a message. Each message has a *label* which contains the essential information for determination of importance and category. Labels display an automatically assigned sequential message number, delivery mode, date and time sent, sender, addressee, subject, keyword(s), and recipients' priorities and other assigned privileges. Normally, individual users have access only to those messages sent or received by them specifically. (Figure 4-3 gives an example of a JENNY message.)

```
                                          JENNY Function:  1

                                          Message NO. 45        Date:  FRI, JAN 14, 1983, 10:15 AM
                                          From:  PETERS
                                          To:  Gaines
                                          Subject:  Washington visit
                                          Text of message:
                                          1 The meeting in Washington with the International
                                          2 representatives went better than expected!
FIGURE 4-3   Example of JENNY function: composing   3 Details will follow upon my return. Cheers!
             and sending a message.                 4 //
```

FIGURE 4-3 Example of JENNY function: composing and sending a message.

The major JENNY functions are:

| SEND | Messages are easily constructed, edited, and sent to other individuals, distribution lists, or to the entire directory of JENNY users. Carbon copies of any message may be sent to three additional individuals or distribution lists. Three delivery modes are available: express, registered, and normal. |

SEND — Messages are easily constructed, edited, and sent to other individuals, distribution lists, or to the entire directory of JENNY users. Carbon copies of any message may be sent to three additional individuals or distribution lists. Three delivery modes are available: express, registered, and normal.

READ — JENNY offers extensive capabilities within the READ function. You may read all current messages including those you have sent and those you have received, or read Pending messages only. Pending messages are those sent to an individual but whose text has yet to be read. You also may read a specific message based on the JENNY message number. In addition, the READ function can locate messages by performing a multilevel "search" based on sender (from), addressee (to), recipients of "carbon copies" (cc:), and the date of message. The date can be specified as either on, before, or after a specific date. Searches may also include subject, tags, or keywords. An individual may elect to direct terminal output to the line printer.

REPLY — Users may reply to a specific message. JENNY knows to whom the reply should be sent. When a user receives a reply, the JENNY "pending message" prompt identifies the specific message as a reply to another specific message. Any keywords associated with the original message are maintained in the reply.

DELETE — Any message accessible to a user may be deleted at any time. The deletion is from only that user's available pool of messages. A message stays in the system until the last owner of the message has deleted it.

TAG — The user may generate a personal filing system by placing tags on any message accessible to him or her. A message may contain a maximum of three tags. The user builds and maintains a unique list of tags which facilitate retrieval of messages.

STATUS — JENNY maintains records of messages associated with a specific user. These records display the number of messages sent and received within each delivery priority. Registered messages which have yet to be read by the addressee are identified, as well as any pending messages.

FORWARD — Any received message may be forwarded to another individual. Identification of the original sender and receiver is maintained.

SPECIAL FUNCTIONS — JENNY has eight special functions which provide administrative and accounting commands and special privileges that enhance the individual user's ability to use JENNY to its full potential. Some of the special functions, such as the addition or deletion of users, changing user privileges, and displaying usage statistics, are restricted to a JENNY system manager. Other functions, such as the creation and mainten- ance of distribution lists, changing personal passwords, and interfacing with files, can be made accessible to all users. Comprehensive reports are available to a JENNY system manager to determine session, message, and function statistics.

AUTO FORWARD AND REPLY	JENNY also provides automatic forward and reply capabilities. Users may designate other recipients for their messages with the option of retaining a copy of the auto forwarded message in their accessible message file. A user may enter a short auto reply, such as "I will be out of town until Sept. 15th," which is immediately displayed to any user sending to another user who has invoked auto reply.

The SEND function does much more than just send a message. It uses *prompts* to lead you through a sequence of steps very similar to those for composing, editing, addressing, and mailing a letter.

A message has basically two parts: (1) the label, which is at the top and includes information on to whom and from whom the message is sent, the date, time, and subject; and (2) the text, where you enter what you want to say.

JENNY prompts you to help you complete the label, and then prompts you for the text. When you are finished entering text, you go to the next line with a "return" and enter two slashes: //.

Figure 4-3 shows how this looks on your terminal.

Now that you are finished with your message text, JENNY will ask, "Do you wish to SEND, EDIT, or CANCEL? (S, E, C)?" If you want to edit, choose that option and JENNY will place you in the JENNY editor. At the editor prompt, you enter a "?" to see the editing commands. To leave the JENNY editor, you enter an "E" (exit).

If you are now ready to send the message to someone, enter an "S" at the above prompt. But, the message isn't gone yet! JENNY needs a few last questions answered, so the following prompts appear:

```
Keyword: International
CC: Brown
Delivery: (? for a list of Delivery Options) R
OK to delete YOUR copy after sending? N
Message #45 sent
```

If you don't have any key words, or CC:s, just enter a "return" and JENNY will move to the next prompt. However, note that you *must* choose a delivery option and decide whether or not to delete your own copy of the message. In the above example the "R" (registered) delivery option was chosen, and your own copy was *not* deleted. Then the message was sent.

The READ function is called by entering the digit "2" or the letter "R" at the "JENNY function:" prompt. This function initiates the reading of a message accessible to the user. Accessible messages are those which the user has either sent or received.

The following example (Fig. 4-4) demonstrates calling the READ function and entering a "?" to display the READ options.

Messages can be read either by specifying the JENNY message number or by satisfying "Read option:" criteria.

```
JENNY Function: 2
Read option(s) (? for a list of options): ?
Valid READ options are:
      PENDING
      ALL
      Or a Message Number
OR: Any combination of the following:  (1 per line)
      FROM          name
      TO            name
      KEY           keyword
      TAG           tagword
      SUBJECT       up to 20-character word or phrase
      ON            date (like:  JUL 4, 1982)
      BEFORE        date
      AFTER         date
      TEXT          causes message text to be displayed
      OFFLINE       directs output to the line printer
      NOASK         suppresses "OK to delete message?" prompt
```

FIGURE 4-4   Calling the READ function.

In order to read a message by number, you specify the message number of the message you want to read. This can be done at the time the READ command is called with the digit "2," or in response to the JENNY prompt "Read option:." When reading by specifying message number, JENNY will display both the message label and the text. Whenever you read the text of a message, JENNY asks if you wish to delete the message.

Figure 4-5 demonstrates one method of reading a message by indicating the message number.

FIGURE 4-5   Reading a JENNY message.

```
JENNY Function: 2
    Read option(s) (? for a list of option): 150
```

```
MESSAGE NO. 150 NORMAL MAR 15, 1983, 9:06 AM
FROM: WILLIAMS, FRED          TO:  SMITH, TOM
SUBJECT: SALES MEETING
_____
The sales meeting scheduled for April 12 has been moved to April 19.
If this presents a problem, let me know.
```

```
OK to delete # 150? (Y or N) N
JENNY Function:
```

If you ask to read a message which has been deleted from the system, or a message which is not accessible to you, JENNY responds with "Sorry, message not found" and returns you to the "JENNY Function:" prompt.

In addition to reading a specific message by indicating its message number, you can select all the messages accessible to you which satisfy any of the following criteria:

PENDING — pending messages
ALL — all messages accessible to you
FROM — name of sender of the message
TO — name of person, or distribution list, to whom message was sent
KEYWORD — is associated with a specific keyword
TAG — is associated with a specific tag
SUBJECT — contains a specific string in the subject
BEFORE, ON, or AFTER a specific date

One of the distinguishing features of JENNY, aside from its personal filing system, is the range of special functions it provides. The JENNY special functions are called by entering the digit "8" at the "JENNY Function:" prompt. These special functions control the administration and accounting activities and other user features which enhance the use and efficiency of JENNY. Some of the features of the JENNY special functions are allocated to specific individuals by the JENNY system manager.

Two special JENNY members are recognized: the JENNY *system manager*, and a JENNY *administrator*. The JENNY system manager is the person who has total administrative authority for the system. By default the JENNY system manager has one implicit capability: He or she can assign a special privilege to other users referred to as JENNY administrators. The JENNY system manager is also the *only* user who can assign billing codes and assign the privilege of not being shown on the LIST command.

A JENNY administrator is often a division or department head who is assigned sufficient privileges to add or remove members and distribution lists on the directory and who performs directory or distribution list maintenance. All members added to the directory by a JENNY administrator are automatically given the administrator's billing code. Figure 4-6 shows the major special functions available under JENNY.

FIGURE 4-6   Display of JENNY special functions.

```
JENNY Function:  (? for a list of Functions) 8

Special FUNCTION:  (? for a list of FUNCTIONS) ?

1. Add or remove individuals and/or dist. lists
2. Change your personal password
3. Directory maintenance
4. Add/remove distribution list members
5. Display usage statistics by billing code
6. Display last log-on for individuals
7. Modify the keyword and/or personal tag list
8. Interface with MPE files
9. Return to the JENNY function prompt

Special function:
```

JENNY provides us with a full complement of tools for electronic mail, including a personal filing system and a mechanism for data retrieval. But its most advanced feature is the recognition of specific human roles within the organization that uses the message system.

Case Study 4: Electronic Mail in an R&D Laboratory

Our fourth case study concerns the Far-West Laboratory for Educational Research and Development.*

This organization is a company which specializes in contract studies for federal and state education departments and which is based in San Francisco. During 1982, Far-West Laboratory used JENNY to create a family of computer files that served to structure message interaction between all the members of the organization. These files are called:

- AGENCY
- BOARD
- CALENDAR
- CONTACTS
- DIRECTORY
- DOCUMENT
- FILE

These names were chosen to make it easy for users to associate the name with the function.

AGENCY is a family of items (located in the JENNY system) that contains information on agencies of interest to the laboratory, its divisions, or programs. This information may include agency names, addresses, telephone numbers, names and titles of key agency personnel, names and dates of laboratory contacts, current or prior relationships with the agency, descriptive information, etc.

BOARD is a family of electronic bulletin boards. It may contain anything that one might want to post on a bulletin board for others to read. Usually these are current notes, news, public messages, announcements, etc.

CALENDAR is a family of items like BOARD on which should be posted only messages about calendars. One can use CALENDAR files to look for dates and times to schedule meetings, conferences, etc. And, of course, the user can post his or her own calendar.

CONTACTS contain information on laboratory staff contacts with persons. These files are very much like the AGENCY family, but they deal with persons. Items in these files will usually be contact forms containing entries with names, organiza-

*I am indebted to Paul Hood for supplying the information included in this case study.

tions, dates, notations, and other information on important contacts with persons outside the laboratory.

DIRECTORY contains names, titles, addresses, telephone numbers, and other notations on persons or organizations. These files can be used to find addresses or telephone numbers, or to check titles or spelling of names. DIRECTORY files will eventually contain a much longer list of entries, but usually with less information per entry than will be found in AGENCY or CONTACTS files.

DOCUMENT contains entries similar to library card files or bibliographic entries. Items posted to those files may contain citations, index "key words" or "tags" and perhaps abstracts, tables of contents, or information on where copies of the document are physically located. DOCUMENT can be useful in preparing bibliographies or in searching for a document. The next family, FILE, may actually contain the text of the document.

FILE is a family of items which may contain correspondence, reports, notes, budgets, personal service agreements, reminders, or any other kind of document one might want to save and retrieve directly through computer search.

Each of these family files is searchable using the full set of JENNY search features. These include:

Date (of message origination)

ON   date (such as December 15, 1982)
BEFORE   date
AFTER   date

Name (of person or file addressed or carbon copied)

TO   name
CC   name

Subject (of message or document)

SUBJECT   you can search for a word or phrase up to 20 characters long within the 50-character limit of the subject line.

If messages or documents are carefully titled, the subject search is potentially the most powerful of all search elements. By making a careful choice of subject descriptors, names, dates, organizations, persons, or other information entered on this line, you can significantly increase not only the power of the computer search, but the ability of the searcher to scan the titles of retrieved documents (especially if there are several) before displaying and reading the text of each document.

In order to restrict the number of key words to a manageable number, the key word list is controlled on an agency-wide basis. The words on the list are chosen (and will be modified over time) to keep this list relatively short and yet powerful enough for a broad variety of laboratory staff search needs.

Tag Words.   Suppose a division, program, or project needs some special words to retrieve items in the files. That is what tag words are for. One can tag any message (document) in a file, *after it has been sent to that file*, with up to three tag words (each up to 16 characters long). Since these tag word lists are associated with individual destinations (your own personal file or a family file), any message *received* in a file can be tagged with just about any word one wishes to use. For instance:

```
Message number to be tagged: 3258 (CR)
Tag #1      ACADEMY  (CR)
Tag #2      MEMBEROPINIONS  (CR)
Tag #3      SITEVISIT  (CR)
Thank you.
```

An internal memorandum regarding the use of the system specifies:

If you give some careful thought to the selection of tag words you use, you can "tailor" the tag word vocabulary of each file you use. Of course, it will be important for all persons sharing that file to keep current on the list of tag words so that all of you can use them, both to tag and for searches of that file.

This company has developed a structure for the use of electronic mail that makes it an integral part of its overall office automation effort.

## CHAPTER 5

TOOLS
OF CONFERENCING

WHAT CONFERENCING DOES

USER-LEVEL FUNCTIONS IN TWO BUSINESS SYSTEMS
(PARTICIPATE AND NOTEPAD)

SPECIALIZED ROLES IN CONFERENCING: EDITOR, ORGANIZER,
FACILITATOR, ADMINISTRATOR

CASE STUDY 5: ENGINEERING CONSTRUCTION

WHAT CONFERENCING DOES

Electronic mail satisfies the need to move messages into mailboxes according to certain priorities and certain distribution structures. But it does not provide a shared communications space to a specific group of people working on a specific task. To accomplish this feeling of shared communications space is the goal of computer conferencing.

Computer conferencing has evolved in a different environment from that of electronic mail. In conferencing, the messages themselves are not as important as the group process which they support. To call this process a "conference" is not good terminology, since this kind of system also carries private (person-to-person) messages that can be filed and retrieved as they could under a mail program. This problem with terminology was recognized almost as soon as "conferencing" was invented in the mid-1960s, but no one has been able to come up with a better word. Perhaps one of the readers of this book will have an idea for a new term.

In Chap. 1 we defined conferencing as the use of a computer message system to define groups of people sharing access to a common topic file through which both public and private messages are exchanged.

A complete example of a computer conference will provide the reader with a better grasp of the process. In June 1973, the author, together with Gerald Aske-vold at the U.S. Geological Survey and Richard Miller and Hubert Lipinski at the Institute for the Future, ran a conference on the subject of geological databases. The participants were earth sciences experts located in Washington, D.C., Denver, Colorado, and Menlo Park, California. There were 10 users, each equipped with a computer terminal. Each user had made a call to the ARPANET and had given a code word which connected him to a Digital Equipment computer running the conferencing system. This computer recognized their names and personal passwords and introduced them into the live discussion.

The first question, raised by a geologist in Menlo Park, involved finding oil pools in Colorado with a production of over 2 million barrels in 1969 and a type "A" sand. The expert who had developed the database system was in Washington. He translated the question into a retrieval request which the whole group could immediately see and check. As soon as an entry or message was typed, it was transmitted to all the participants. The team in Denver had another terminal linked to the petroleum database, in Los Angeles. They obtained the answer to the question and announced it in the conference. At the same time, the team in Menlo Park was answering questions about mineral properties in Alaska, the answers to which were stored in the Stanford computer (see Fig. 5-1).

This conference, held over 10 years ago, demonstrated how a computer network could link together a group of people dispersed over the whole country, and draw on the resources of several centers of information and expertise.

An exchange of electronic mail messages among the participants could have accomplished the same results, but would have taken days or even weeks. Direct access to databases could have given the geologists the answers they needed, but it would have required giving them specialized training. Here, people could simply ask a question, watch their colleagues discuss and rephrase it, and receive the answer in real time. The group could then discuss its significance.

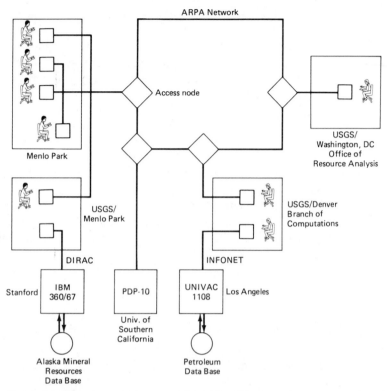

FIGURE 5-1 The computer conference of June 7, 1973, which linked together experts at three branches of the U.S. Geological Survey and two databases on mineral deposits and oil wells.

Current conferencing systems allow users to merge database results with program calculations and forms. Mathematical models and expert systems can be invoked within the structure of conference messages. Results can be saved, placed on record, or communicated to selected people by private messages.

What about the case where users are in several countries, separated by many time zones, and do not find it practical to "meet" over the network in simultaneous fashion at a particular time? In this situation they can simply "attend" the conference at their leisure! The system brings them up to date and gives them the opportunity to review previous entries, make their views known to the group, and leave again. Such extended use is called delayed, or "asynchronous," conferencing.

USER-LEVEL FUNCTIONS IN TWO BUSINESS SYSTEMS (PARTICIPATE AND NOTEPAD)

In this section we will review two systems in actual commercial use. Both are available through a network, which means that users can access the service by making a local telephone call anywhere in the United States. Foreign users connect themselves to a national network that has a gateway into the corresponding U.S.

network. They are billed by the postal authority of the country for the total time used.

We have chosen to discuss two commercial systems rather than features of the various research facilities in existence, because the former give a more precise indication of those functions people actually use when they have to pay for a system. Research organizations are heavily subsidized by such sources of funding as the military or the National Science Foundation, which have played a key role in the early development of the technology. Their experience is not always transferrable to the business world, because users who are willing to experiment with certain functions when they are nearly free are not the users who demand daily performance and reliable productivity in an industrial situation, and when a sizable cost is attached to the function. Both, of course, are vital to the future development of the field, but our orientation in this book is clearly to the business world. Relevant information on research systems can be found in the literature of the field, and much of it has been summarized in an often-quoted book by Turoff and Hiltz, *The Network Nation* (7).

The PARTICIPATE system

This system operates on the Source, an information utility (available through the GTE/TELENET network) that runs on PRIME computers.

First-time users provide their name, address, phone number, and a description. They can also set their terminal's width and the type of prompt they want (long or short).

The system maintains an "in tray" for each user. If there is information waiting, a user can read, scan, batch, or hold. The READ command will print out each item at a time and give the user the opportunity to do something with it. The SCAN command lets a user choose how much of each item he or she wants to see on the first pass. In BATCH they all come at once with no pauses. HOLD leaves them for next time.

When you read or scan waiting items, you will be prompted for a "Disposition?" that allows you to answer, reread, rescan, read or scan related items, join an item if it is defined as an "exchange" or an "inquiry," or go on to the next item.

The next prompt is ACTION, after which you can:

WRITE	into a scratchpad for later sending
READ	text items (or READ ABOUT someone)
SCAN	
JOIN	to become a participant in a discussion of an inquiry or exchange
LEAVE	is the reverse of JOIN
ORGANIZE	converts an inquiry you have written into an exchange for which you are now the organizer. This means you can determine who has "read access," as opposed to "write access" and how long items are saved, provided you pay for storage charges.
MODIFY	lets you change anything
QUIT	takes you out of the system

An *inquiry* is the basic unit in PARTICIPATE. You create one from your scratchpad by beginning a line with ".I" and sending it to one or more individuals, or to an exchange, or to another inquiry.

Inquiries can be joined by others who want to receive automatically all answers to that inquiry. "Inquiries with a lot of answers are, in effect, conferences," says the PARTICIPATE user's manual. The system also allows messages, answers, exchanges, and announcements.

An *exchange* is an organized inquiry where the organizer controls storage purge cycles and read-and-write access for any announcement, inquiries, or messages with their associated answers.

In summary, PARTICIPATE is a message system which allows group interaction about specific inquiries. It is a conferencing system to the extent that inquiries can be joined by users who can respond to them.

The NOTEPAD System

NOTEPAD is available from Infomedia Corporation in San Bruno, California. It is accessible by computer terminal from the United States, Canada, Europe, and the Far East on a 24-hour basis through the international network of Tymnet. The system addresses the project management and group coordination needs of organizations. It is used primarily where there is a need to coordinate messages and information sent between geographically dispersed project teams. A project team member in one location can send instantaneous messages to all team members in all locations. He or she can also send private notes to selected team members.

NOTEPAD stores messages until the recipient is ready to accept them, and automatically files messages in predefined files. NOTEPAD may also be used for simultaneous or nonsimultaneous group conferences and discussions.

A NOTEPAD account consists of a number of discussion topics or files called "activities." A typical menu of activities that a user might see upon entering the system is shown in the list below.

1. General discussion
2. Engineering
3. Construction
4. Administrative services
5. Suppliers
6. Subcontractors
7. Planning and scheduling
8. Procurement
9. Coordination

When a user signs onto NOTEPAD, the above list of activities is displayed. The user selects an activity and reviews any messages or discussions that have taken place since the last access. The user then enters any response pertaining to that activity. These remarks are immediately transmitted to all members of the project team participating in that activity.

Messages can be public entries, going to all participants, or private notes, transmitted only to selected participants. Some NOTEPAD activities have a thousand names listed as participants.

The system keeps an audit trail of all messages and information in an activity. Only the project organizer may delete public entries. Individual participants may delete their private notes. Messages can be retrieved later by author, date, key words, message number, or any combination of these.

NOTEPAD can be used from most video display and hard-copy terminals from many worldwide locations through local telephone calls. Most personal computers and some communicating word processors such as Wang and Lexitron can also be used to access the system. Lengthy information can be typed on the word processor, edited, corrected, and then transmitted to a participant.

NOTEPAD is easy to learn and use. It can be learned in less than an hour. There are nine basic commands on a paste-on strip which is attached to the terminal. These nine commands correspond to the numbers 1 through 9 on the keyboard. To write a note, strike a "1"; to read a note, strike a "2," etc. (see Fig. 5-2).

The secret to the simplicity of using NOTEPAD is the command strip which fits over the first row of keys on any keyboard, essentially providing the participant with a built-in user guide.

Programs may be developed in PASCAL, FORTRAN, BASIC, or COBOL and interfaced with NOTEPAD. Once the program is compiled, it can be saved in such a way that any user may run it (under the "Service" action) or that function may be reserved to the organizer or to the administrator.

Three levels of security passwords protect access to the project and the privacy of user information. A special STATUS command enables users to determine the last time a participant or group of participants signed on to the activity. This function also enables users to see if the latest entry was read by the activity participants.

NOTEPAD offers additional features for project members who wish to perform tasks related to eliciting information, voting, or running specific programs.

The "Ask" feature collects and processes responses to a question. Participants may "vote" on an issue, and the system can display the "Feedback" to the author of the question in the form of a graphic chart (as shown in Fig. 5-3).

The "Run" feature allows participants to run a special computer program available to the project members in an activity. For example, on a construction project, the field material requisition form was entered into NOTEPAD as a special program. Project team members could call up the form, "fill in the blanks," and transmit the completed form to the home office. Once a program is run, the results may be used as part of a public entry or sent as a private meassage to another user.

FIGURE 5-2   The NOTEPAD "Command strip."

NOTES		SELECT	ENTRIES		SPECIAL ACTIONS			QUIT
WRITE	READ		WRITE	READ	STATUS	EDIT	SERVICE	
1	2	3	4	5	6	7	8	9

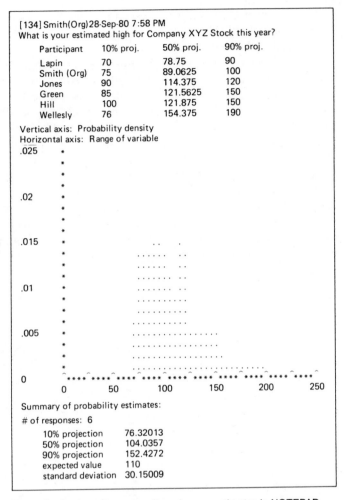

FIGURE 5-3   Example of automatic aggregation of group estimates in NOTEPAD.

SPECIALIZED ROLES IN CONFERENCING: EDITOR, ORGANIZER FACILITATOR, ADMINISTRATOR

Whenever people assemble to solve a problem or discuss an issue, certain roles emerge within the group: Someone calls the meeting, defines the agenda, reserves the room. Someone introduces the speakers, takes notes, and records the votes and decisions. Someone else makes sure proper procedure is followed and that no one goes away mad because his or her views were ignored, or because no time was allocated for an item deemed relevant. And one person usually dominates the public proceedings because he or she has most of the facts available about the issue at hand, although that person may not have the authority or the support of the group in the decision at hand.

Any computer-based message system that ignores these natural roles is calling for disaster. Not only should these roles be recognized, but special functions must be allocated to the people who fill them.

In the early days of message systems when programmers were the only users, any message text in a group mailbox could be edited by anyone. That was appropriate as long as the users formed a tight-knit team of technicians with a very high level of trust. However, in situations where tricky negotiations were involved or when differing views had to be reconciled, you could not rely on transcripts of the system: Any group member could have made the deletions and additions he or she liked. Users also often complained that anyone could see anybody else's messages.

In a more advanced system such as NOTEPAD, the *editor* is the only person who can change the group record. There is also an *organizer* who has the power actually to *create* activities by designating the title and the list of initial participants and indicating if the activity is open to all comers or restricted to a closed group. In the latter case the organizer is the only person who can add members or remove members from the list.

FIGURE 5-4   Roles within a computer conference.

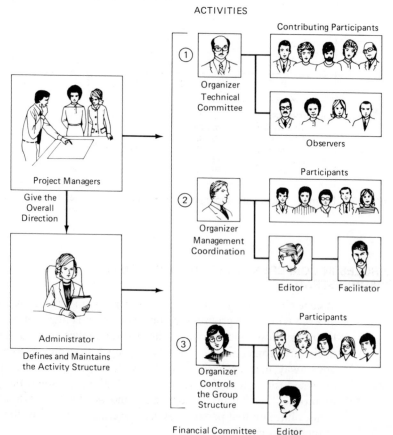

The organizer can also inhibit private communication in cases where all group interaction has to be "on the record." And the organizer can change roles of group members. He or she can designate some of them as observers—people who can read all the entries in the record but cannot send public messages.

The *facilitator* is a group member who has special skills rather than special powers. The facilitator uses these skills to help participants get acquainted with the rest of the group, to keep the discussion focused, and to make sure every point of view is represented. This work is usually accomplished through private messages to individuals rather than by group messages.

Figure 5-4 shows the roles played by the leaders within a structure of conferences. Clear definition of these roles allows a system like NOTEPAD to mesh smoothly into the existing structure of an organization.

Administrators have access to the whole file system with a NOTEPAD account. They can also obtain usage statistics by user or by activity, and monitor project costs in that fashion.

The clear definition of participants' roles is even more important in conferencing than in electronic mail because there is a wider range of behaviors to be supported. Therefore, systems should not be evaluated on the basis of cost alone, or of software features, but on the adequacy of the fit between the system and the existing organizational culture.

Case Study 5: Engineering Construction

It is perhaps in the major engineering construction firms—companies such as Kaiser Engineers, Bechtel, and Fluor in the United States, or Schneider, Framatome and Schlumberger in Europe—that the need to coordinate project teams over vast distances and many times zones is most actually felt.

Projects developed by such companies range from the building of mining plants, refineries, and electric generation plants to the erection of entire cities, harbors, and airports in places where palm trees or wild beasts were the only signs of life before their arrival. Office automation in its traditional sense has little to offer these projects, although they entail budgets in the millions or even billions of dollars per year. Communications, filing, retrieval, and computation are essential, but there is no way to reach all the group members by tying together word processors in local area networks. The time required to train operators of typical office automation equipment is prohibitive. Project managers need hands-on access to a reliable, simple system.

This case study summarizes the experience of one particular company with the NOTEPAD system over the first 18 months of its use, mainly in the development of mining projects.

In June 1980, office automation experts within this company contacted the manager of several mining operations to assist in the selection of a pilot group for the NOTEPAD system. He selected a gold mine construction project with a strict time schedule and critical communications needs. The project jobsite was located 70 miles from Ely, Nevada. Two radio phones, shared with the client and 200 contractor personnel, provided primary communications between the jobsite and the home office management team. Mail services required a minimum 2-day turnaround. Field personnel were housed 70 miles away from the jobsite and commuted by bus morning and evening, creating a severe communications problem. The main opportunity for the managers to obtain information from the field was at night in person-to-person telephone calls between their homes and the project team at the motel.

Approximately 15 persons, including the project manager, construction manager, operations manager, group supervisors, and representatives from administrative services, procurement, and planning and scheduling were trained to use the NOTEPAD system. In addition, supplier, subcontractor, and client personnel were also trained. Each user had access to a terminal, and the operations manager used a portable terminal from his motel room in Ely to send information to the home office.

During the initial 3-month pilot test, 900 messages (78 percent public entries, 22 percent private notes) were sent between the project team members. The major impact of the system was on management control, both at the home office and in the field. Headquarters personnel were impressed with the increased ability to document the progress of the project. They could give instructions to the entire group, and respond rapidly to engineering and procurement decisions. When a key manager had to leave the project for 2 weeks, he stayed in touch with the team via NOTEPAD. A quick scan of the activities on the system brought him up to date on the project.

Personnel in the field also reported saving valuable time. They were able to communicate their needs more effectively and get every decision clearly documented. They could enter progress reports directly into the system at their convenience, while they had previously been forced to wait until evening to call managers at home to discuss the day's progress (see Fig. 5-5).

The project was completed 5 days ahead of schedule. Managers reported saving 1-worker-day per working day in the home office and the field because of NOTEPAD.

At the end of the initial 3-month pilot test, a preliminary evaluation was completed. Because of the favorable response NOTEPAD rapidly expanded from a small controlled pilot project to a full-scale production environment on nine mining projects and one pipeline project.

In 17 months, 250 participants used the system for 2477 hours. Over 12,063 messages have been transmitted, and 113,465 entries and private notes have been viewed by the participants.

The general conclusion of the pilot tests is that an electronic messaging system significantly improves communications between project teams and remote locations.

In addition, the users concluded that:

• NOTEPAD offers a variety of time-savers for users—instantaneous communications between geographic locations, reduced interruptions from telephone calls,

- Construction
    - Weekly activity reports

- Engineering
    - Changes
    - Design problems

- Scheduling
    - Milestone reporting
    - Problem solving

- Cost Control
    - Actual vs. Budget
    - Status of incurring costs

- Procurement
    - Expediting
    - Logistics

- Inspection
    - Physical inspection
    - Contractor tests
    - Safety analysis
    - Quality control

- Subcontractors
    - Progress reports
    - Cost reporting

- Client
    - Change orders
    - Progress reports

FIGURE 5-5   Typical structure of NOTEPAD activities in engineering construction applications.

reduced turnaround time on urgent decisions or actions, and access to a permanent searchable record of all messages.

• Messages and information transmitted on the system are often sent at lower costs than on long-distance telephone calls, Telexes, facsimile, and other conventional media.

The project manager also commented favorably on the resulting savings in paperwork. At the beginning of the operation, based on past experience, he had ordered four filing cabinets with four drawers each to hold administrative and management files. As the plant was completed, only two had been used, and he reported that the message system had allowed him to save half the time he usually devoted to administrative communications.

## CHAPTER 6

ANALYSIS OF GROUP COMMUNICATIONS

CAPTURING GROUP USAGE AND COST DATA

In a computer message system, the *session* is perhaps the most convenient unit to which measures can be attached. A session begins when a user logs in to the computer; it ends when he or she logs out. Simple? Not quite. From the user's point of view the session would last exactly the period of time that his or her terminal is connected. However, the user's connection is made first through a network, and only later to the host computer where the message system resides. The two measures should differ only by a few seconds, but in actual practice the differences may be larger. The network may fail to establish the connection altogether. Or it may fail to disconnect at the end.

Once the user's terminal is actually connected to the host, nothing prevents the user from exercising various programs before and after he or she uses the message system. So the network session is different from the computer session (often called "the job"), which can be different from the message session. And within the message session a single user may engage in several activities—entering and leaving various conferences, for example. We are taking the point of view of computer conferencing for purposes of this chapter, because measures applicable to electronic mail also apply in conferencing.

We have adopted a compromise which defines the unit of system usage (the "session length") as the time spent by one user in one conference activity (see Fig. 6-1).

The system will record two sessions for this user, each corresponding to a conference activity. In general, each activity represents a different group.

This is only one way to define the situation, of course. Systems that have a more complicated structure will demand more detailed measures.

What can we quantify about the session? There are 16 measures that we can readily obtain (see Fig. 6-2).

In addition, a full systems analysis would also determine if access was direct or through a network, what the speed of transmission was, how many disk accesses were made, etc. However, these measures are not essential to our purpose in understanding group communications, so we will omit them in the present discussion.

FIGURE 6-1   Network, job, and message activity time line.

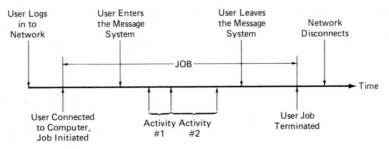

1. Starting date and time
2. Ending date and time
3. Total duration
4. Use of commands or functions
5. Number of public messages sent
6. Number of private messages sent
7. Number of public messages received
8. Number of private messages received
9. Total messages sent
10. Total messages received
11. Words in public messages sent
12. Words in private messages sent
13. Total words sent
14. Participant identifier
15. Activity identifier
16. Number of users present simultaneously

FIGURE 6-2 Quantifiable measures readily obtained for each session.

Along with session data we will also compute cost data, which will be aggregated on a monthly basis by activity. The main components of the cost are:

1 Total connect time
2 Use of storage media
3 Use of computer resources (processing, use of channels, etc.)

The overall result can be presented on the basis of a cost per user, or a cost per hour, or a cost per word. We saw an example of this technique for the NASA groups in Case Study 2.

From such session data we can derive higher-level information about participants, as shown in Fig. 6-3.

Once these measures have been established, we can begin tabulating data that will tell us how the system has been utilized. Figure 6-4 shows an actual example of such a tabulation when the NOTEPAD system was introduced into one test project in an engineering firm. Usage for June (the first month) was distorted by the presence of observers and by temporary training activities, a pattern which was expected. The training activities were deleted in July.

FIGURE 6-3 Participant statistics (per activity and per month).

1. Public messages sent
2. Private messages sent
3. Public verbosity (average number of words)
4. Private verbosity
5. Time per session
6. Rank by public messages in the group
7. Rank by private messages in the group
8. Use of commands
9. Total number of sessions
10. Total time spent

ACTIVITY INDICATORS	JUNE (training)	JULY	AUGUST
# Participants	12	9	13
# Hours	74	42	48
# Sessions	741	518	734
# Messages Sent	367	266	307
# Synchronous Hrs.	11	1	4
Hours/User	6.2	4.6	3.7
Sessions/User	62	58	56
Sessions/Hour	10	12	15
Minutes/Session	6	5	4
Messages Sent/User	31	30	24
% Private	26%	17%	23%
% Typing Time	45%	53%	40%
Word/Message	68	73	69
# Quits (Log-Ins)	255	240	296
Sessions/Log-In	2.9	2.2	2.5
Minutes/Log-In	17	10	10
Log-Ins/User	21	26	23

FIGURE 6-4   Actual example of NOTEPAD system utilization. (Credit: *L. McLorg*)

From the data in July and August we can see that the typical user in this company comes into the system once a day, stays approximately 10 minutes, and attends two group activities during that time. Approximately one-quarter of all entries are private.

From these statistics it is possible to derive a measure of total information transmitted in the form of total messages received: A public entry is seen by all (N) participants, while a private note is seen by only two persons. Figure 6-5 shows the results in the present case.

The total number of messages transmitted among the group during the 3-month test is 8754. Since total system usage represented 164 hours, the average partici-

FIGURE 6-5   Information transmission statistics.

		June	July	August
No. Participants	N =	12	9	13
Public Entries	E =	272	221	237
Private Notes	P =	95	45	70
Messages Transmitted E X N + 2P =		3454	2079	3221

pant was able to receive 53 messages per hour of system use. (This figure does not include messages that could be *recalled* from the activity record.)

It is even more interesting to observe how users progressed in their use of the system, since the number of messages transmitted per hour of system usage was only 47 in June and 50 in July and climbed to 68 in August—or more than one message a minute—clearly showing the strength of this medium of communications.

USER-LEVEL STATISTICS: MESSAGE DISTRIBUTION AND PARTICIPATION RATES

When the system has been monitored for a few months, the analyst is literally swamped with data which needs to be aggregated and displayed in a few simple ways before their meaning can emerge. In our work we have found it useful to complement the usage and cost statistics mentioned earlier with some user-level data which are displayed in graphic form for greater convenience.

The participation rate within the group is the most direct way to display the use of the message system. In Chap. 2 we alluded to the fact that groups of human beings seemed to allocate face-to-face interaction according to a negative exponential curve. (Figure 2-5 shows the distribution in *The Taming of the Shrew* by Shakespeare.) This curve was noted by sociologists Stephan and Mishler in their work on small groups and it has remained a standard feature in most computer conferences.

Figure 6-6 shows the distribution of participation rates within a group of educators who used a computer conferencing system during 1974. Such a distribution, however, does not give us a detailed feeling for the individual differences within the group. In particular, it does not conveniently display the way in which different individuals use private and public messages.

FIGURE 6-6   Participation map for an education conference.

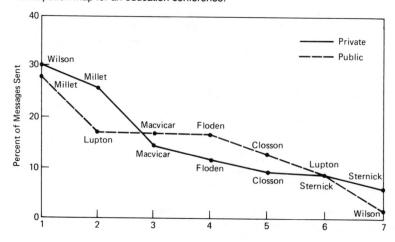

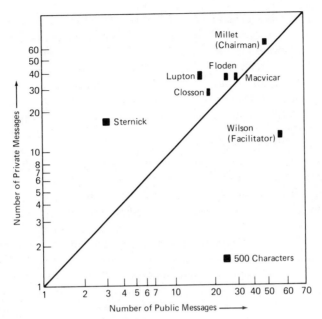

FIGURE 6-7   Distinction among roles for a group of educators.

In order to explore this issue further we introduced the idea of a participation map as a tool for the graphic display of group intersection through computer conferencing. In such a display we plot the position of the most active participants by showing the number of their public entries versus the number of their private notes, so that those points above the first diagonal represent people who tend to be more public than private in a given activity, while those below the line tend to be more private, a fact usually associated with the particular role they are playing in that activity.

In addition, each participant can be shown as a rectangle proportional to the average length of messages and entries (verbosity).

Figure 6-7 shows a simple participation map for the same group of American educators. Here for the first time we can see a clear distinction among the roles played by various individuals in a computer conference. Mr. Thaddeus Wilson, who served as facilitator, remained in the private part of the map, while the chairman of the conference was at the top of the public scale. The participation map shows the *reality* (rather than the subjective perception) in the use of a message system.

REACTIONS AND PERCEPTIONS OF GROUP MEMBERS

Now that we have learned how to capture relevant session data and aggregate it according to cost and to group activity and roles, how can we relate these measures to the actual perceptions of the individuals within the group?

To establish such a connection we need to interview users in a systematic way. We can also capture their open-ended comments, or ask them to fill out a questionnaire. During the 1960s one group of British communications experts developed a useful research instrument at the Communications Study Group in London. Called the "Description and Classification of Meetings" (DACOM), it involved obtaining the reactions of users of new media (such as audio conferencing) on a seven-point scale ranging from "unsatisfactory" to "satisfactory." The questionnaire was tabulated according to a series of 12 types of activities, from "receiving information" to "bargaining." Sociologist Robert Johansen has applied this instrument to computer conferencing with useful results. Figure 6-8 shows a typical set of reactions from two managers in a mining operation. They were clearly satisfied with the use of the message system for information exchange, exchange of opinions, and inquiries. They were not satisfied with the system in situations involving persuading, bargaining, and resolving disagreements.

Various questionnaires have been designed to elicit information from users, addressing their general reactions to the system, the impact it has made on their work and on other forms of communication, and some specific aspects of group dynamics, such as perception of others and feelings about access to colleagues.

By themselves these pieces of information do not necessarily mean very much. But when they are correlated with other participant-oriented measures, they provide useful insight into the way a system is used. This information is vital to avoid introducing a message system into situations where it is likely to be detrimental to the work of the group. On the contrary, it can define situations where message systems will have a positive impact and will be perceived as useful tools. Several practical examples of the use of this technique will be described in Part Three.

FIGURE 6-8   Typical DACOM responses. The two respondents are in agreement and their answers are consistent with the observation that a system such as NOTEPAD does not replace the telephone or face-to-face communications for complex interpersonal tasks such as bargaining.

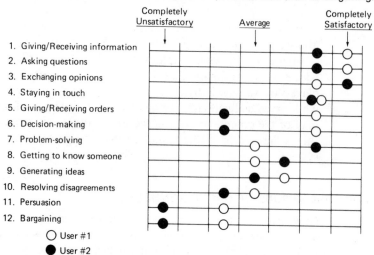

Case Study 6: The U.S. Geological Survey

1 International Exchange of Mineral Data Bases

As in many scientific disciplines, specialists in the earth sciences are scattered throughout many countries. The need to exchange information on geologic formations and mineral resources makes collaboration among these groups an essential requirement of economic life. The geologists who compile and maintain mineral databases constitute a significant international community. Many of them have used message systems such as NOTEPAD and its predecessor, PLANET, to support their work.

The first such international conference was in preparation for a Paris meeting of the Committee on Storage, Automatic Processing and Retrieval of Geological Data (COGEODATA). This is a committee of the International Union of Geological Sciences, with members in Canada, England, Sweden, Denmark, Norway, the Netherlands, and the United States. The committee began using PLANET with a discussion preparing a workshop in London, and two major meetings at UNESCO in Paris in November and December 1975. This conference not only rescued the Canadian organizers of the meetings from a long mail strike, it also helped the participants define the agenda of their discussions and resolve numerous technical details.

Surprisingly, the use of the conference continued to grow rapidly during the meeting, when all the participants were together in Paris but felt a need to "stay in touch" with their home base. A second computer conference, centered around the need for international standards for computer files in resources studies, was also initiated. *To our knowledge, this use of PLANET represents the first instance when networking has been used to prepare and follow up a major international face-to-face meeting.*

The follow-up conference focused on an important Canadian document related to the standardization of mineral and fuel deposit data. There was not adequate time in Paris to resolve the numerous issues raised at the UNESCO meeting. The conference thus became a convenient meeting hall for the scientists after they returned home. The discussion often consisted of the exchange of views with a single user in the system at a time, and this activity was supplemented with simultaneous brainstorming. On one occasion, no less than 11 geologists from five countries debated a particular standard among themselves for 2 hours. The final document was drafted, finalized, and approved through the message system.

Another outgrowth of the Paris meetings was a conference discussing implementation of a database program first developed to serve the needs of U.S. geologists. Its use for a large collection of oil and gas records in Colorado suggested that it deserved a larger audience. Accordingly, a PLANET conference was created to distribute the system outside the U.S. Geological Survey. The participants have represented the Geological Survey of Canada, the Netherlands Soil Survey, and their counterparts in France, Newfoundland, Great Britain, and other countries.

The geologists involved in these conferences—some of which lasted more than

2 years continually—have reported the following benefits: the ability to engage in joint writing and in the sharing of data; easy access to effective communications while traveling; flexibility in preparing, organizing, and following up major meetings; creation of entirely new channels for dissemination of scientific data; effective group problem solving; and the extension of working hours—an important feature for a community whose communication activity spans 10 time zones around the earth!

The dots in Fig. 6-9 indicate the locations of major centers of geoscience research where the message system has been used for communication with scientists in Canada and the United States. The map clearly shows the need for a form of communications that creates a common space for the exchange of ideas and facts without requiring the cost and complexity of frequent meetings.

2 Group Management of Projects in Alaska

The development of economic and industrial resources of remote regions is another task to which a conferencing system is uniquely suited. When Congress considered

FIGURE 6-9   Early users of PLANET in geoscience.

the Native Claims and Settlement Act, it mandated a number of projects that required coordination between groups in Alaska and various experts and managers in the rest of the country. The U.S. Geological Survey has used PLANET to implement its operations under this mandate.

Under the Native Claims and Settlement Act, lands designated as "d-2" areas—national interest lands—were to be closed to mining. An assessment of their mineral potential was imperative. Several Survey groups were involved in the project, notably in Reston, Virginia; Menlo Park, California; and Denver, Colorado, where the geochemistry group was located. The system was used to link mineral economists, geologists, and field workers together in long-term exchanges that would help them make the most of the short time when teams could be deployed in Alaska each summer.

The severe weather conditions in Alaska require very effective scheduling and optimum logistics in the preparation of field work. Delays of a few weeks in the arrival of equipment or in the exchange of information can mean a delay of a whole year in a given project. The system was helpful in providing everyone with a precise and easily retrievable record of technical information among Survey teams. It also made possible the opportunity to gather opinions and analyze estimates given by field geologists in discussions with their remote colleagues.

Some examples of actual exchanges give the flavor of the conferencing activity: One typical message read:

> We should figure on 45 days of helicopter beginning July 1, with a good chance of a 10-day extension. That means 135 hours with a possibility of 30 hours' extension.
>
> I figure that at last summer's rates it would take you 135 hours and 30 days to collect 600 samples in Philip Smith, plus about 15 hours extra for lost travel time if we work from Happy Valley.

The geologists often used the medium to confirm data sent by mail or to place other discussions on record. For example, one scientist commented on data he had mailed to his colleagues:

> I have just sent you a hand plot of the zinc values for the Chandalar quad and have done some crude anomaly outlines. It seems that there are two belts of zinc values running east–west along the northern edge and one roughly through the middle. I would like to know what you make of this.

The time and distance barriers caused by the remoteness of the working sites in the wilderness of Alaska made the system a natural choice for project managers. It made possible the free flow of information, not just from one person to another, but among a group of coworkers spread over many time zones.

Telephone communications to Alaska are both expensive and unreliable. Mail suffers long time delays. With the establishment of computer network access, conferencing has begun to play an important role in providing an alternative to some information exchange situations, and a supplement to other media.

During the first quarter of 1978, the typical monthly cost to link one participant to the conferences was under $120, a very small expense when the costs of travel, equipment, and support system are considered for a person working in the field.

The experience of the geologists in Alaska can be extended to many other groups: construction teams, engineering projects, real estate developments, and transportation or energy undertakings.

3 Projection of Commodity Prices and Reserve Estimates

A demonstration of the potential of computer conferencing as a basis for future expert systems was conducted during the Circum-Pacific Energy Resource Conference attended by mineral economists and energy experts from all countries and was held in Honolulu between August 22 and August 29, 1974. Nine specialists, who were familiar with the different subjects of the inquiry, were asked to estimate the average December 1974 price for gold, silver, copper, aluminum, and gasoline. These experts included:

- A mineral economist from the USGS
- A geologist from the USGS, active follower of gold prices
- A commodity expert
- A geologist, USGS, well-read consumer
- A USGS branch chief, mineral resource expert
- A geologist with a Canadian mineral resource company, formerly a metals commodity specialist
- A USGS geologist, specialist on South America
- A mineral resources expert from Mexico
- An economist on the Institute for the Future staff

All participants were provided with information on current price history, including average prices for June 1973, December 1973, March 1974, and June 1974. The probability elicitation function was used to prompt them for future values. The resulting forecasts, together with actual high, low, and average figures, are shown in Fig. 6-10.

What we see here is a system that can take human judgment, quantify it with probabilities attached to a numerical value, and aggregate it at the group level. As we have observed earlier, the same system can also interact with databases and with mathematical programs, formatted information, and models of various processes. An environment is being created in which artificial intelligence and human knowledge can find a common ground and can be quickly applied to the solution of actual industrial problems.

4 Conclusions

Over the life of the conferences we have mentioned, extensive statistics were obtained about cost, message exchange, and user reactions. These statistics were then correlated among themselves to determine the overall usefulness of the message system. The insight that was gained from these surveys can be summarized in seven points:

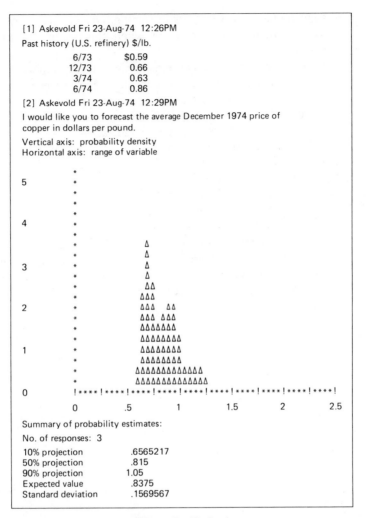

```
[1] Askevold Fri 23-Aug-74  12:26PM
Past history (U.S. refinery) $/lb.
              6/73        $0.59
             12/73         0.66
              3/74         0.63
              6/74         0.86
[2] Askevold Fri 23-Aug-74  12:29PM
I would like you to forecast the average December 1974 price of
copper in dollars per pound.

Vertical axis:  probability density
Horizontal axis:  range of variable
```

FIGURE 6-10   Sample transcript from the Circum-Pacific Conference.

• Computer conferencing provides users with the potential to tailor their work style and life-style to increase their freedom from current office constraints. In the geosciences both the personal inclinations of many researchers and the requirements of field work make this increased freedom attractive. At the same time, it can represent a threat to existing bureaucratic structures.

• Computer conferencing can play an important role in humanizing and augmenting computer technology. For many scientists who have not used computers before, it serves as a simple yet useful introduction to other services such as text editing, database retrieval, and modeling.

• The use of computer conferencing does not necessarily promote sharing and cooperation, although such effects may be intended by its users. Instead, it tends to augment the collective work of small groups that have a high need to preserve a record of their activities, even when this means additional psychological constraints.

• Computer conferencing seems to reveal latent communication patterns. These latent patterns may be positive—consider the emergence of invisible colleges—or they may be negative, revealing disharmony, rivalry, and potential feuds. In this sense, computer conferencing might act as a mirror of *actual*, as opposed to *theoretical*, power structures within an organization.

• It can be used to keep groups of workers informed about changing resources. Catalogs, bulletins, and inventories require constant updating and reprinting. Effective use of a message system would save this expense.

• For many groups, computer conferencing can facilitate the implementation and dissemination of software. It can be especially useful in advertising, maintaining, and assisting in the use of databases or any software activity which is dynamic in nature, if the intended users are widely disseminated.

• Computer conferencing can reduce the need for increasingly scarce and expensive office space. On the other hand, such office decentralization will pose a threat to the traditional manager, who is likely to feel a loss of control over subordinates.

MANAGEMENT OF MESSAGE SYSTEMS

INTRODUCING
AND FACILITATING
NEW APPLICATIONS

LEARNING

ORGANIZATIONAL PATTERNS

LONG-TERM ISSUES AND OPPORTUNITIES

CASE STUDY 7: THE 1982 OFFICE AUTOMATION CONFERENCE

In the first and second parts of this book we examined the need for message systems and various tools available to the person who is charged with filling this need in a particular organization. In Part Three, we will review what is known about the management of message systems, starting with the ways in which learning takes place. Then we will examine how different organizations make use of these tools, and will raise questions about the longer-term effects of the systems on business and industrial work. We will study the application of message systems to both large and small organizations. Some organizations will be centralized; others will be loose associations of groups or individuals. Some will be technical; others will be oriented toward the humanities, law, religion, social concerns, or lobbying.

As you may guess, it is impossible to make a general statement covering the application of message systems to such diverse organizations. In most cases, however, it is wise first to introduce the message system to a small group having a high, defined need for the form of communications offered. The system should be viewed immediately as a tool that will be evaluated on its cost effectiveness and its merit. Setting aside technical aspects of communications, we find that considerable care should be taken to match the system to the organizational culture in which it will be operating. This will be done by creating appropriate subgroups and setting up leadership roles, if those already exist in the orgnanization, or assisting in the creation of consensus groups or informal discussion circles, if the participants do not have a traditional structure.

Along with this cultural mapping, a facilitator should be designated. As mentioned earlier, the facilitator has no special power over the group. If someone talks too much, to take an extreme example, the facilitator cannot remove or interrupt the participant. However, he or she can influence the group, make individuals aware of the reactions of others, encourage them to remain focused on the task at hand, and generally assist them as they move through the various stages of learning.

Finally, the technology should be carefully picked to support the type of communication the group needs. Word processors, personal computers, and even the executive workstations now flooding the market are not designed with communication in mind, so that a significant hurdle has to be overcome before the user can become a participant in electronic mail, conferencing, bulletin boards, or any other form of communication through computers.

Once the initial group has learned the system, its experience can spread to other groups, and the entire organization will reach a point where it has mastered the tool. That does not mean, however, that the system is fully utilized, or that two similar organizations will use it in the same way. And even when the application is fully mature, issues raised by the system will force many managers to rethink traditional techniques they may take for granted. It is impossible to improve the way groups communicate without raising fundamental questions about the evolution of human structures and their leadership and management. Although it is not the purpose of this book to answer these questions, it is important to warn the reader of their existence.

LEARNING

Use of a message system is a personal experience which can be greatly influenced by a dynamic individual in the role of facilitator or organizer. The concept of facilitator parallels that of an integrating agent as introduced by John Bennett of IBM Research in the context of decision support systems. Bennett observes that "the user correctly perceives that the system is very different from any of his current sources of information. He will find that working with the system requires that he learn a new way of thinking."

One element in this new way of thinking has to do with the need to type. Users may adapt to this difference easily, or they may find it initially threatening, depending on their past experience and skill in typing. The second change is that the medium is no longer assumed; the medium is not transparent, or immediately grasped. As mentioned earlier, a computer terminal presents unusual keys and switches with strange symbols and names. There is a coupler for the telephone and an unseen computer many miles away. These new symbols, switches, and equipment must be explained simply, but not condescendingly, to the new user before communications can begin.

Most interactive systems, compilers, word processing software, and accounting packages are introduced with the help of a bulky user's manual and several tutorial sessions. Given the environment in which message systems are operating, this approach is not practical. We have to accept the challenge of designing the medium for very busy, impatient users who cannot afford the time to read a manual and are too far away geographically for a face-to-face tutorial. We have to rely on human facilitation, extreme care in interface design, and a concise user's manual.

How much and what information the facilitator gives the new user depends on how confident the participant is in his or her ability to learn and adapt. "The new user," according to Bennett, "faced already with an overload as he enters the confidence phase, needs access to information which contains all (and only) what he needs to know . . . so that information overload is avoided." After an introductory telephone conversation with the new user in which the facilitator explains how to access the system network as well as what password and codes are necessary, one can start the learning process using the medium itself.

Since the most common type of message sent and the easiest to initiate is the public message, the facilitator tells the user to communicate in this mode for the first few entries. Figure 7-1 is an example of the initial interaction between the facilitator and the user. Here, Thad Wilson, a member of a research team at the Institute for the Future, was the facilitator.

In this example, the user (a social scientist at an east coast university) is completely unfamiliar with the terminal and questions what is appearing on his transcript, as is shown by entry [3] in Fig. 7-1. A technical problem is discussed, but the user does not know what to do and is not even certain that his messages are received.

In Fig. 7-2, the user is turning to the facilitator for assistance through the system itself.

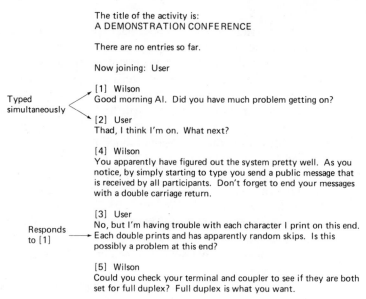

The title of the activity is:
A DEMONSTRATION CONFERENCE

There are no entries so far.

Now joining: User

Typed simultaneously

[1] Wilson
Good morning Al. Did you have much problem getting on?

[2] User
Thad, I think I'm on. What next?

[4] Wilson
You apparently have figured out the system pretty well. As you notice, by simply starting to type you send a public message that is received by all participants. Don't forget to end your messages with a double carriage return.

Responds to [1]

[3] User
No, but I'm having trouble with each character I print on this end. Each double prints and has apparently random skips. Is this possibly a problem at this end?

[5] Wilson
Could you check your terminal and coupler to see if they are both set for full duplex? Full duplex is what you want.

FIGURE 7-1 An example of an initial training session.

At the end of the training session, arrangements are made for a follow-up, as shown in Fig. 7-3.

In entry [35] in Fig. 7-3, the facilitator is intentionally signing off so that the user will get a system-generated message that the facilitator is "now leaving." From now on, the user is on his or her own (Fig. 7-4).

Messages [34] and [36] in Fig. 7-4 are sent before the user has realized that the facilitator has left. The concept of talking "to myself" (in [38]) seems initially strange but apparently is "socially" accepted in this medium. The user continues in good humor in an effort to learn more, attempts to understand commands that will be useful to him, and lastly, sums up his introductory experience: "This is fun."

For a facilitator to be effective (more precisely, to increase the learning rate and self-confidence of the new user), he or she must be prepared for circumstances that will be unique to the particular user's personality and propensity to learn. This task is especially difficult when users are experts—that is, highly respected, recognized

FIGURE 7-2

[6] User
Did you receive my last message and questions?

[7] Wilson
I'm receiving your messages correctly (no double characters). Let me know about the duplex settings.

[8] User
Have checked coupling; it's okay, but don't know how to ascertain the full duplex setting. Any suggestions?

[32] Wilson
Next time, do exactly the same as you did this morning, remembering "FD" for duplex setting.

[33] User
I'm about ready to sign off, as soon as I receive reply to my query no. 30. Will hold sign-off till I hear from you to do it.

[35] Wilson
O.K., Al. Thanks for taking time during your lunch hour for this demonstration. I'll talk to you later this week.

FIGURE 7-3

authorities in their own field—whose time is valuable and who may be inhibited, frustrated, or intimidated by the terminal. (Many users have never used a terminal before. Some are frankly antagonistic to computers, and especially to the concept of computer-based communication, which they expect to find dehumanizing).

Although most initial interaction follows the above pattern, there are exceptions. Figure 7-5 is the last part of an exchange in which the user and the facilitator had difficulty in understanding each other. The interaction had been confusing to the user and frustrating to the facilitator.

The unexpected answer to entry [46] in Fig. 7-5 and the subsequent caveat in [48] were valuable information for the facilitator. Earlier in the demonstration he had assumed too much about the user's knowledge of the system and had offered too much information based on this false assumption. In summarizing the facilitator's or integrating agent's objectives, Bennett states, "The agent must be keenly

FIGURE 7-4

[34] User
Super. Doesn't seem to require too much of the user, but this test is most helpful. When I know you are not there to help, however, I hope I don't panic. If I should, I'll just type "help" and hope that it will get me going again.

[36] User
Thanks for your time, too. Much appreciated. With much thanks. Al

[37] User
On Monday, I'll plan to start in the system by calling for a review of status. I presume there'll be some type of updated agenda to get us underway.

[38] User
I guess you're already out. I presume that now I'm just talking to myself, but as long as this is okay, I'll continue for a few more minutes and see what happens.

[39] User
I'd now like to make a mistake and try to correct it.

[43] User
I want to add this statement and then check status again.

[44] User
One more correction. This is fun.

[42] User B
Are you there? Would I know if you left?

[43] Wilson
The system will notify each participant when someone else leaves or enters a
conference.

[44] Wilson
By accessing the system and then typing the word "STATUS", you can find out
what each other participant has seen in the conference.

[45] User B
Shall we quit now?

[46] Wilson
What has given you the most problem so far?

[47] User B
You

[48] User B
You and I ask and answer, respectively, different questions. I suspect I am typical
of the other participants, and you will have to anticipate that they will not think
in the same way you do.

FIGURE 7-5   Example of user frustration in learning.

perceptive of user needs and responsive to user difficulties in system use. *He will
be continually impressed with how little is reliably known about helping people
manage their own learning process.*" [Our italics.] Like Bennett's integrating agent,
the message system facilitator is "chiefly guided by intuition and experience."

The role of facilitator in a message system begins to change as participants
become familiar with the characteristics of the tool. At that point, the facilitator
becomes less a teacher and more a guide and assistant in the proceedings. He or
she may be called upon to act as a human translator of the machine's behavior,
particularly in the case of system or network failures. And as things get fully under
way, the facilitator will make suggestions about how the medium can best be used
to accomplish the tasks. He or she might suggest, for instance, that the organizer
send a private message to several key participants about a particular issue under
discussion. Also, the facilitator will periodically check with various participants
to see if they are having any problems using the system to express their own points
of view. Examination of the private message traffic to and from the facilitator in
one computer conference, as shown in Fig. 7-6, reveals both the informality, the
humor, and also the very critical skills which characterize the facilitator's function.
As is clear from this example, the function of facilitator is an important and varied
one, which might be performed by more than one person within the group.

It is interesting to examine an entire task (for example, a complete computer
conference) and classify the various statements according to various categories. As
we saw in Chap. 2, it is possible to go through the transcript and recognize messages dealing with learning as opposed to procedural issues (setting of agenda,
forms of address, priorities). It is also possible to recognize statements of personal
positions ("I think we should do X") and statements of integration ("perhaps a
compromise between X and Y would be the following decision . . . ").

Private message [20] to Terry
Welcome back, Margaret. Never let a machine overcome Yankee ingenuity.

Private message [23] from Terry
Joanna's name appears but no messages seem to follow. Is she transmitting?

Private message [32] to Sharp
Why don't you break in on Joanna and advise her to send her message in bits and pieces.

Private message [33] to Terry
You might, at a propitious time, announce some recess for lunch and schedule an afternoon regrouping. A. West should be coming on around 1:30 EST. I leave the recess decision in your hands.

Private message [34] to Terry
I think it might be sage, in view of the inconsistency of the network, that maybe you discuss the agenda schedule for September as that is probably most important now.

FIGURE 7-6   Example of facilitator functions.

From our observations, learning and procedural statements occur first, but they tend to reach a point of saturation. On the contrary, substantive messages start later (position first, integration later), and rise more quickly without reaching saturation. By following these trends (Fig. 7-7) it is possible to determine what point the group has reached in the discussion or resolution of an issue. Good facilitation, naturally, should help one eliminate or minimize the learning messages (by ensuring that all participants have been trained previously) and the procedural messages (by reaching prior agreement on agenda, issues, and rules for the group). As an

FIGURE 7-7   Evolution of four different categories during a computer conference.

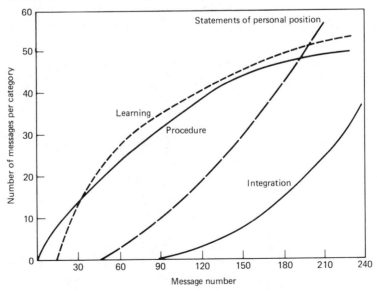

organization becomes more familiar with the message system as a tool, these concerns become less important. Participants can get down to business right away in later sessions.

The use of private messages (as opposed to messages sent to an entire group) is another important factor, both in individual learning and in organizational learning. In Fig. 7-8 we show the percentage of private messages sent by an average user as a function of his or her experience with the system.

As participants learn the capabilities of the message system, they gain flexibility in the use of personal interaction. Typically, private message use increases from 30 to 40 percent of all messages—not a dramatic rise, but it does indicate that private messages are not a transient phenomenon in one phase of learning, but a permanent, integral part of group communications.

This obviously creates problems for the traditional organization which exercises close control over the communications of its employees and which has strict rules against personal use of corporate tools. In one series of computer conferences sponsored by an agency of the U.S. government, the management met after the first month of usage to review utilization statistics. When it was discovered that one-third of all interaction was private, the senior manager complained that private messages were like personal phone calls, and that the government should not be paying for them. He felt that the whole thing was due to the fact that the conference was composed of both government employees and independent contractors, who had different things to discuss when negotiating with each other. Accordingly, he requested that a special government conference and a separate contractors' conference be created. When the group met again the following month, it was discovered that the proportion of private messages was the same in all the groups, and was still about one-third. In other words, when the government employees were in a group by themselves, isolated from contractor personnel, they still felt the need for private communications in support of their work. This observation has been verified many times since this first experience.

FIGURE 7-8 Effect of learning on private message exchange.

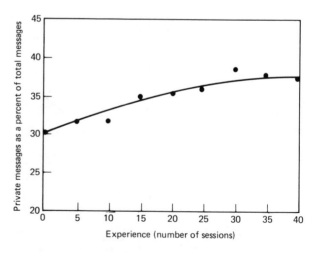

Another way to track the introduction of a system into a group is by *semantic analysis*, which is very time-consuming and demands access to a transcript or at least parts of transcripts. It involves a careful study of the use, order, and frequency of words in messages. This technique is based on contributions from Pittinger, Hockett, and Daheny (8) and from Edwin Schneidman (9). The former have used microscopic content analysis to successfully infer from an analysis of the first 5 minutes of a tape-recorded psychiatric interview certain aspects of an individual's cognitive styles from an inspection of written or spoken text. Finally, Laffal's (10) method of word association analysis, which often reveals implicit levels of meaning in a transcript, has also provided a basis for our study (11).

This approach involves three key assumptions: First, a generalization and basic principle is that everything communicated is meaningful; that is, all aspects of the transcript are to be considered. Second, meaning and pattern in communications are culturally based and then mediated by the individual person, the communication situation (e.g., the medium, the task), and the others in the situation. Third, communications may be about the topic, but it is also about the communicators themselves, about the situation, and about an immediate concern. Furthermore, a list of possible subjects to which participants are likely to respond or refer in any communications would include:

- The topic of the discussion, usually overtly
- Ordering or structure messages
- Feelings and emotions regarding the individual himself or herself, the topic, the discussion or the process of communications, and another participant
- Personal relationships (e.g., roles) or group relations

These may occur in questions, answers, information, offers, emotional responses, and many other forms. The subjects are not necessarily overt and a part of the surface line of the written text. Indeed, the first two are usually the surface content, and the others occur more implicitly in choices of words, sequencing, and other linguistic subsystems. Our analysis has sought to uncover such communications.

In applying this technique to transcripts, it is important to note the characteristics of the message system. The author of an entry has the option of editing or rewriting his or her contribution to any extent desired before it is entered into the transcript. The author may alter a misspelling, rewrite the entire entry, prepare it in advance, or even cancel it. Thus, we are not necessarily reading a spontaneous comment. Instead, there may be several layers of revision based on writers' wishes to clarify, add evidence, impress themselves or others, protect themselves, or take into account reactions of other participants.

Editing also occurs in face-to-face communications, but it is internal. We do not know whether there would be more or less editing in writing compared with speaking, or whether the individual is consistent in the amount of editing he or she does, regardless of the mode or the context.

Also, because computer conferences are usually circumscribed in subject matter, there is pressure on participants to stick to the topic. Depending on the number of participants, their acquaintance with each other, and the public nature of the conference, the number of personal and extraneous messages will be affected. In an open, many-participant, subject-labeled conference there will likely be greater formality and logical consistency, and fewer emotionally toned messages.

One other factor will affect the content of the transcripts: the physical requirements of the system itself. A computer terminal is slightly different from a typewriter in arrangement of some keys, in the touch required, and in the time delay of the printing. These factors all require some adjustment on the part of the user, and until a user feels comfortable, he or she is likely to be self-conscious and perhaps hesitant with entries. In the same manner, if typing itself is slow, or if there is self-consciousness regarding it, then we would expect entries to be more selective, less frequent, and also shorter, and so not necessarily reflective of the total reactions of the participant.

These qualifications all point to areas in which we must make assumptions about factors affecting the communications process. There is almost no research (hard or soft) on these issues. For that reason, we have to rely on assumptions drawn from our present store of experience. In summary these are:

1 Message systems provide fewer channels of communication than face-to-face communication does. They require that messages be coded into written or printed symbols.

2 The channels lacking in message systems are those typically concerned with regulating ongoing interaction, and those which communicate feelings, intentions, and personal relationships.

3 However, messages of the type mentioned above are implicit in the written channel to some extent, overtly and covertly. They may be brought out through various techniques of analysis.

4 The point of analysis is the submitted entry, after editing (if any) by the participant.

5 Private messages are assumed to be relevant to the public record and where available should be correlated with the main discussion.

6 Initial unfamiliarity with the system will affect the number and length of a participant's entries, but there is a gradient of learning which leads to a level of relative ease for most persons.

ORGANIZATIONAL PATTERNS

At a workshop on the design and use of message systems Professor Estrin of UCLA once remarked, "We cannot assume that patterns of usage will be stable within an organization until several months have passed, and even for long-term users there may be some phenomena that take place only after one year, two years, or longer."

With these remarks in mind it is useful to summarize what has been learned, first in an R&D setting, and later in an industrial setting, among groups that used message systems for 1 year or more in support of specific tasks. This analysis shows that some features of usage become very stable across organizations. There are other features for which no pattern develops.

Among six organizations that used a message system for 6 months to 2 years in a research setting, for example, we found that no pattern developed in the rate of public or private message sending (Fig. 7-9 and 7-10).

Similarly, there is no uniformity in the use of editing characters (Fig. 7-11). Some organizations were fastidious in their editing. Others simply did not care; they sent messages complete with misspellings and repetitions. As user terminals become more and more sophisticated, including word processing features, text editing, and spelling checkers, the pressure to send "perfect" text may increase. Some people argue that some of the quality and spontaneity of human communication may be lost in the process. Messages may become as formal as a "letter to the editor" in *The New York Times*. The analysis shown in Fig. 7-11 certainly shows that the need for text editing is not a universal constant: It is perceived very differently by different organizations.

When we look at session duration, we begin to see a pattern emerge (Fig. 7-12). After 18 months of usage most organizations had converged to an average duration of 8 minutes per session. This value is obviously affected by cost and technology. As communications costs rise and as personal workstations acquire the capability to capture text locally and send it in short "bursts," the duration of sessions may drop. Equally important is what we are *not* observing: We do not see the emergence of a class of high-level "knowledge workers" spending hours at their terminals to use message systems. Most users go in, get the information they need, respond to it, and get out to turn to other tasks.

FIGURE 7-9   Organizational patterns in public message-sending rates.

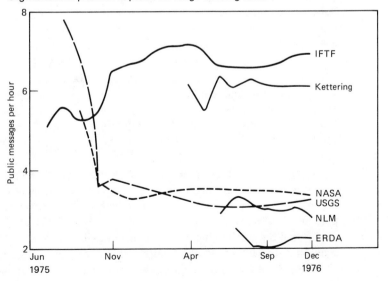

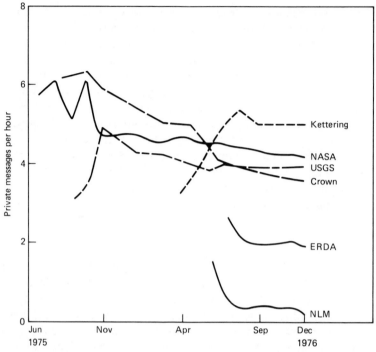

FIGURE 7-10 Organizational patterns in private message-sending rates.

Another pattern emerges when we look at the ratio of private to public messages, which converges to a value of about 50 percent, meaning again that about one-third of *all* messages were private. Among the organizations shown in Fig. 7-13, the exception was NLM, the National Library of Medicine, where the organizer prohibited the use of private messages—again out of a concern that they represented personal communication for which the sponsor should not be paying.

The other side of this coin appears when we look at a variable we have called "public verbosity"—the average length of public entries. Most organizations converged to an average length of 65 words per message. There was, in fact, surprising agreement among institutions as diverse as NASA and the Kettering Foundation. The exception was the National Library of Medicine. When the ability to send private messages was turned off, the participants compensated by sending much longer public entries (see Fig. 7-14).

Next, we should examine the use of message systems outside normal office hours. When we have studied groups that had casual access to terminals both at home and the office, and were encouraged to use them, we found that nearly 40 percent of all sessions occurred outside the 8-to-5 weekday working hours. This means that the participants had increased flexibility in their work hours and (in the opinion of the author) worked more and better (Figs. 7-15 and 7-16).

When we studied larger groups in traditional organizations, on the other hand,

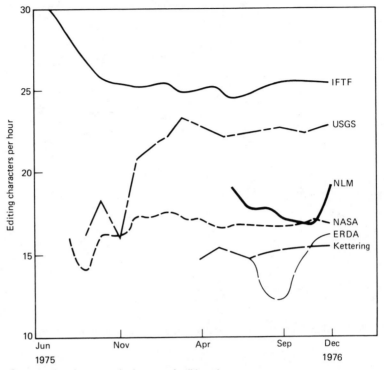

FIGURE 7-11   Organizational patterns in the use of editing characters.

FIGURE 7-12   Organizational patterns in session duration.

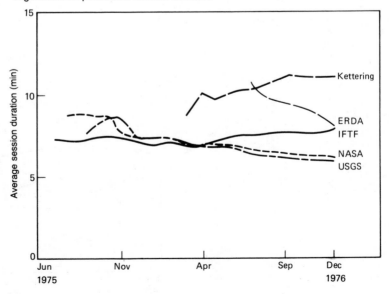

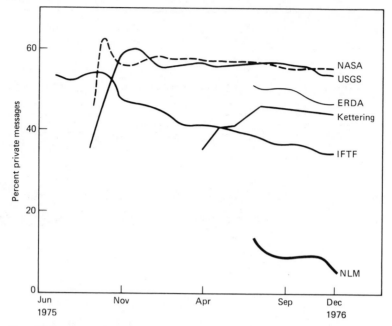

FIGURE 7-13 Organizational patterns in the ratio of private to public messages.

FIGURE 7-14 Organizational patterns in public verbosity.

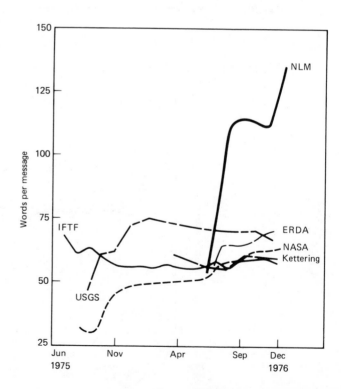

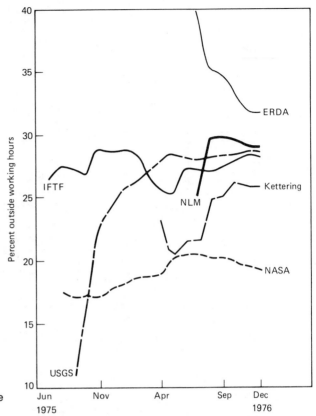

FIGURE 7-15 Organizational patterns in time spent outside working hours.

we found no such effect. Use of the system corresponded closely with the workday, although there was indeed an increased opportunity of communication for those organizations spread over several time zones, as we saw earlier in the case of NASA.

While the above observations were based on groups using early message systems in an experimental setting, they are confirmed and extended by more recent experience. The electric utilities that have applied NOTEPAD to their work have found that private message sending increased dramatically, while the overall use of the system grew across the many organizations that used it. In a 1-year period (1980) the percentage of public messages fell from 62 percent to 33 percent, while the total number of messages grew from 600 to 2100 a month, and the number of users increased from 65 to 167 (at this writing the number of users exceeds 1000 for this single application).

The high volume of private messages was examined; five basic reasons were found to explain it.

1 As new users were added to the network and trained to use the system, these training sessions distorted the statistics because they include a high proportion of private facilitation messages.

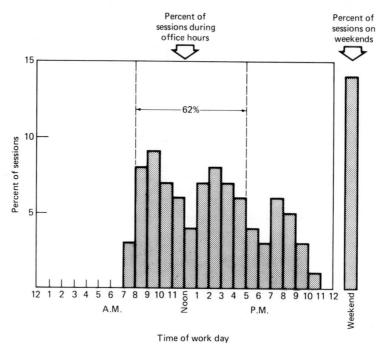

FIGURE 7-16   Distribution of participation of six users across a 24-hour period (based on 1155 sessions).

2 Users were asked to report all operating problems by private messages. Similarly, information on system features was given that way, to keep the group record free of information that has no general value.

3 New participants were often reluctant to put information on record because they weren't comfortable with other group members until they developed a feeling of trust by working with the group.

4 As the size of the user community increased, the probability of a synchronous encounter also increased. Such encounters encourage private message exchange, as we will see in the next chapter.

5 With the accumulation of new information, there was growing pressure to place on record only those messages that are truly useful to the entire group, and to deal with all secondary issues in private messages. This is an effective way to guard against information overload.

What is a normal level of private messages for a group using a computer message system? It is hard to answer this question with any generality, but we have observed that among the applications we studied, the most successful groups were those with slightly more public than private messages, and where two types of leaders clearly emerged:

• The organizer or chairperson of the group consistently had a high number of public entries.

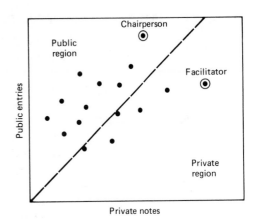

FIGURE 7-17

- The facilitator had a high number of private entries.

When the position of the users was plotted on a participation map we would expect to find the situation shown in Fig. 7-17. Note the separation between the roles of the chairperson and the facilitator, and the fact that the majority of users are found in the "public region" of the map, with perhaps 55 to 70 percent public entries.

In a map such as that shown in Fig. 7-18, we would guess that the user community is not homogeneous. In fact, it is probably split between a group of "substantive" participants (A) and a group of people involved in private negotiations (B). This might be typical of a crisis conference. Or it might indicate that a subgroup of the community has a topic of interest that is not expressed or allowed on the public record. In either case, we would not expect such an activity to last very long, unless some exceptional facilitation skills were applied.

Private messages are essential to the dynamics of a group. They are a medium for releasing tension, establishing trust, continuing training, expanding the topic of discussion, expressing new ideas, and enriching contact with colleagues.

FIGURE 7-18

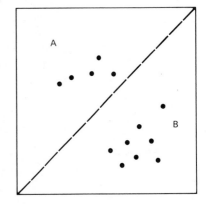

LONG-TERM ISSUES AND OPPORTUNITIES

Let us assume that the message system has now been introduced successfully into your organization. It is used by hundreds, perhaps thousands, of people every month. What are the new issues likely to emerge from this situation? What new opportunities are created?

Perhaps the most obvious issues are those of group control and information control. Although they are best left to specialists in organization behavior, these issues manifest themselves through requests to accommodate the needs of the group in new ways: creating subgroups, introducing new features, expanding control of participation lists or key words, enabling users to list all their messages at unattended workstations for later reading and response, creating new ways of filtering messages, and providing various means of interacting with user-supplied software that may reside in a personal computer or in another mainframe.

A study performed at the Institute for the Future* pointed out that within organizations, the person who pays for computer terminals and time could control access to the medium, and others may resent this control. Furthermore, if participants owe their presence in the system to the organizer or a funding officer to whom he or she reports, they may feel limited in the types of contributions they can make. While the costs of message exchange may drop sufficiently to discount this potential policy issue, such a drop seems unlikely at this time. The same study went on to list several important issues:

> The recorded nature of computer messages and the existence of usage statistics imply serious potentials for the violation of personal privacy.

Computer message systems are a text-based medium, with the text stored on a computer in machine-readable form. There are distinct advantages to having a continuous written record of proceedings. However, this same characteristic provides the opportunity to take statements out of context or "read between the lines." For instance, a joke or a series of social exchanges in a computer conference may be very important in maintaining the vitality of a group (as they often are in face-to-face meetings), but they could be made to appear wasteful or childish if quoted out of context. Such exchanges, of course, happen constantly in human communication; but in a message system they are more available to be scrutinized and misinterpreted.

Also, the ability to collect usage statistics on computer conference sessions poses real potential for misuse and even violations of privacy. For instance, use of participation statistics as a personal performance indicator, while it may be valid to a limited extent, can lead to serious misinterpretations about a person's productivity. Another area of possible misuse concerns the private message feature, since both the level of private exchanges and the identity of persons exchanging them can be tracked unless strong guidelines are enforced.

* R. Johansen, R. DeGrasse, and T. Wilson, "Group Communication through Computers," vol. 5, *Effects on Working Patterns*, (Institute for the Future report, 1976).

There is no evidence that message systems necessarily lead to broadened participation in group meetings. Specific policies will be needed to encourage a diversity of participation.

Computer message systems make it possible for geographically dispersed persons to form working groups. This implies greater potential for diversity of input
and participation by users from smaller, more remote organizations or branches.
Furthermore, the exclusiveness of "invisible colleges" might be diffused to allow
broader participation. It is *also* possible, however, that electronic invisible colleges
will be just as exclusive as nonelectronic ones; invitations to join a particular computer conference group, for instance, could become as prized as memberships in
exclusive country clubs.

Broad participation is not inherent in the medium, although it may be allowed
by it. For example, while computer conferencing provides the potential for regular
contact among geographically dispersed researchers, there are obviously limits to
the number of people who can work together in a given conference group. Thus,
the technology of the medium opens an opportunity for redefining the criteria for
selection of working group members, but it does not automatically ensure diversity.
Policy decisions are necessary for this purpose.

Before explicit policies on the use of computer message systems are developed,
it seems likely that the medium will be used effectively by some individuals to
bypass *existing* group membership channels. For instance, junior researchers could
gain status very quickly by building a network of national or international colleagues not normally accessible to junior staff. Such individuals might also have
easier access to superiors through computer conferencing than through the normal
channels of secretarial appointment-making.

More flexible work arrangements raise questions regarding supervision and
evaluation of workers.

Computer message systems have some characteristics that could be useful in
developing new supervisory procedures. For instance, computer conferencing can
allow a manager to keep up with the activities of a number of groups without great
time and travel expenditures. Although some researchers suggest that managers
have inherent preferences for verbal over written media, Robert Johansen reports:

Several project managers used PLANET for administrative functions during field tests.
One took a "low-profile" approach by simply tracking the progress of several of his
groups and occasionally making comments himself. He told us in an interview that this
provided him with an informal idea of what was happening in the groups. If he required
formal reports, all he got was the formal—and less informative—positions. Another
manager took a stronger role and made specific requirements of the groups he was
supervising. He used the medium in a more hierarchical way to give specific directions
and make sure all the groups were up-to-date in their activities. It appears that both of
these management approaches are possible using computer conferencing, and the choice
may have most to do with the participants and the subject matter involved.

The flexibility of message systems allows greater diversity of working hours and places than is currently the case in most research environments. This flexibility has several implications. "Office hours" could become redefined for many people, thus redefining the process of supervision. Also, people may choose to communicate only during certain portions of the workday while working without interruption during other periods.

The degree of control that a manager has over a group seems most likely to decline if message systems are used extensively. A worker could develop an active network of contacts outside his or her own organization and engage in communications of which the manager has little knowledge. Of course, managers could limit participation in such exchanges or even secretly monitor what is happening. But such tactics would take a great deal of effort, as well as open the manager to a considerable amount of criticism.

Computer message systems raise questions about the structure of office communications, the nature of job descriptions, and decisions about location of employees.

Computer conferencing restructures both the way in which people communicate with each other as well as the opportunities they have to communicate. This restructuring has tangible implications in the possible substitution of one medium for another and, on a broader level, suggests that new communications activities will develop among people. There will be cases (e.g., simple information exchange or question-asking) where a direct substitution of media will occur, while the communications process itself remains essentially unchanged. Broader impact will result from the new or changed opportunities for communications which the message system provides.

The experience with attempts at decentralizing the office has not been very encouraging so far. Not only has the Internal Revenue Service changed its mind several times on the question of allowing deductions for an office at home, but employers remain very uncomfortable with the thought of losing personal contact with workers. Use of home phones for business is frequently questioned or disallowed rather than viewed as a productivity enhancement. Yet there can be no access to a computer message system without some form of phone communications.

Along with these management issues computer message systems raise some concerns from a legal viewpoint. Each organization, naturally, will have to seek specific advice, depending upon the nature of the information it handles, the various classes of users, and the rate structure it applies to its services. With this caution in mind, the following points should be mentioned.

Computer message services raise antitrust issues because they may be exposed to charges of improper anticompetitive activities. For instance, a system used by several companies in the same industry could become a vehicle for collusion. The second exposure is by subpoena of message system records for use as evidence in public or private suits against a particular user.

Privacy issues may be raised under local, state, national, or foreign privacy laws applicable to message systems. At the international level several countries have data protection laws and laws that restrict transborder data flow.

Protection of proprietary information, availability of the service during an emergency, compliance with government regulation, and defamation are topics which should be covered by the proper disclosures and disclaimers.

Suppose a user employee sends an angry message into the system, changes his mind, tries to delete it, and fails. The message is subsequently brought to the attention of management, and the employee is fired. Can he sue the developer of the system, claiming it was negligent in constructing the software so that he could not erase an unread message?

Copyright issues are raised by the potential for message systems to support electronic journals. If A sends a message to B, does the information belong to the sender or to the recipient? The answer varies from country to country. It will be an interesting day in court when this issue is raised about computer message systems.

In the use of NOTEPAD the question of the right of the client organization to list all messages, including private messages, has been raised several times. It is reasonable to take the position that public messages should be available to the client organization and anyone it designates, but that private messages should remain inviolate as the personal property of those exchanging them. However, this view has never been legally tested.

Case Study 7: The 1982 Office Automation Conference

In order to compare the perceptions of participants with the actual use of a message system, Ruth Smith studied a group of people who used NOTEPAD to coordinate and plan the 1982 Office Automation Conference held in San Francisco in April of 1982. This group used NOTEPAD for approximately 9 months prior to the conference and met the profile of a typical application.

There were 50 participants listed in the system. Of these, approximately 20 were the really "active" participants. The others used NOTEPAD for various periods of time and to various lower degrees during the duration of the project. There were six separate conference activities, not including individual, temporary training activities. Activities were broken down into the tasks that needed to be performed to bring together the Office Automation Conference—operations, publicity, registration, special activities, integrated issues and case studies, local media lists, and coordination.

After the project was structured, several participants were trained by Infomedia. Others were added to the conference over the course of the project without the benefit of such training, which may have affected or caused their low usage of the system.

To document attitudes of users, a questionnaire was developed and administered. It consisted of seven questions requiring subjects to respond on a 5-point scale and one last question that called for open-ended comments. Question 1 ascertained the approximate length of time the subject actually participated in NOTEPAD. Question 2 dealt with the subject's perception of his or her own amount of public and private communication. Question 3 allowed subjects to compare themselves with other participants according to the total time of NOTEPAD usage. Question 4 requested the number of activities each subject had access to. Questions 5, 6, and 7 dealt with perceptions of accuracy, feelings of group interaction, and feelings of access to colleagues, respectively.

The questionnaire was distributed by mail, with the exception of Infomedia employees, who received the survey in the company mailbox. Of the 43 participants surveyed, 29 (67 percent) returned the questionnaire and constituted the sample.

After the questionnaires were returned, the method of study was that of relating the data collected from the subjects to the statistical data captured by the teleconferencing analysis program within NOTEPAD. A graphic analysis technique comparing the dependent variables (perception of public to private communication, feeling of access, feeling of group interaction, comparison with face-to-face meeting) was applied to the database. This enabled Ruth Smith to compare systematically the users' perceptions of their participation with the activity, actually measured by the statistical package (see Fig. 7-19).

Analysis of the data leads to the following observations:

The conferences were clearly dominated by two participants, namely, Puehse and Siart (Fig. 7-20). Their roles within the OAC were conference chairperson and publicity, respectively. This finding tends to confirm that computer-based media, like face-to-face groups, can be dominated by a few individuals.

A large majority of the subjects (55 percent) felt the accuracy of a statement made over NOTEPAD is similar to or greater than that of a statement made in a face-to-face meeting. The number of public entries made does not seem to affect the response. The same chart was plotted for private notes, and the results were consistent.

FIGURE 7-19

OAC CONFERENCE HIGHLIGHTS — 1-JUNE-81 TO 31-MAR-82
50 PARTICIPANTS — 16 OF THEM HAD MORE THAN 100 SESSIONS — 25 OF THEM HAD MORE THAN 40 SESSIONS
7060 SESSIONS, 689 HOURS, 4522 MESSAGES (PUBLIC: 1393. PRIVATE: 3129) IN 44 WEEKS.
89 HOURS OF SYNCHRONOUS USAGE
AVERAGE TIME SPENT IN NOTEPAD: 14 HOURS PER PARTICIPANT AVERAGE SESSION DURATION: 6 MINUTES AVERAGE MESSAGE LENGTH: 72 WORDS

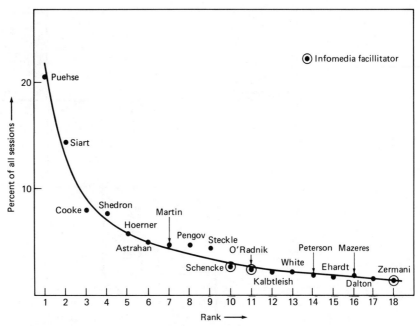

FIGURE 7-20   Participant ranking by sessions.

The perception of interaction increased with the number of public entries made by participants. This is what we would expect in a meaningful, active discussion. However, no attempt was made to compute a level of statistical significance for this observation.

The greater the total number of hours spent in NOTEPAD by a user, the greater feeling of "access" to colleagues that user reported.

Subjects were more positive in their feeling of access to colleagues than in their feeling of accuracy of NOTEPAD, as compared with face-to-face meetings.

The greatest cluster of people felt "accuracy" in NOTEPAD is about the same as in face-to-face meetings, but access to colleagues is superior in NOTEPAD.

Figure 7-21 poses the question of whether people accurately perceive their own participation in terms of public vs. private messages. Conclusion: Most subjects thought they were more "public" than they really were.

Figure 7-22 poses a similar question in terms of perception of one's ranking within the group when total time on the system is considered. The conclusion is that most subjects do not accurately perceive this variable. Most participants have a higher use of the system than they believe when compared with the whole group. The total number of hours spent by most users is higher than they think.

The study, although its conclusions are informal, supports the proposition that computer conferencing provided the group of experts planning the Office Automation Conference with greater access to their colleagues, while offering the same accuracy as face-to-face meetings.

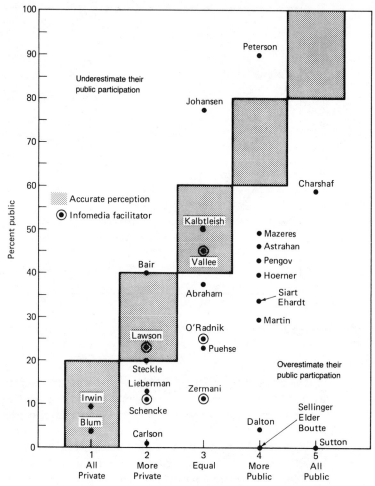

FIGURE 7-21 Feeling of public participation vs. measured public participation. (Credit: *R. Smith*)

We can summarize Smith's observations in the following statements:

1 When it is properly introduced into an organization, computer conferencing provides greater *access* to group members while offering potentially the same *accuracy* of communication as face-to-face conferencing.

2 The feeling of access and interaction seems to increase with greater use of the system.

3 Distribution of participation does not differ significantly from what the literature describes in face-to-face meetings.

4 Participants misjudge their own participation behavior. They tend to be more "private" and spend more time in the system than they think.

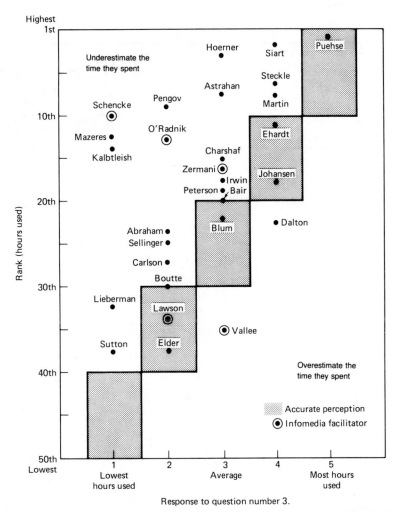

FIGURE 7-22   Perceived ranking in terms of hours vs. measured ranking in the group. (Credit: *R. Smith*)

The study also included a provision for open-ended remarks by the participants. Some of the comments made by the subjects included the fact that NOTEPAD "virtually eliminated telephone tag" and "the easy broadcast meant no one was left in the dark." While users equipped with 1200 baud modems had no complaints about access, several participants noted that using a message system at 300 baud was frustrating when a rapid pace of exchange was desired. They found the transmissions "unacceptably slow." This limitation is a function of the terminal used and will be removed as faster, inexpensive units become available.

## CHAPTER 8

THE SPECIAL CASE OF SYNCHRONOUS COMMUNICATIONS

APPLICATIONS OF LIVE CONFERENCES

When a message system is used at the same time by two or more participants, the resulting situation can be called a "conference." Everyone is aware of others entering or leaving, and messages appear on the terminals of users as soon as they are finished. Some message systems such as NOTEPAD are designed to facilitate this kind of interaction. One user may be reviewing past messages or getting ready to type a new one, when suddenly the notice "Now joining: McFarlane" appears on the terminal. This signals the fact that McFarlane is available for direct communication if other users desire. A third, fourth, or fifth participant may join in real time.

This form of message exchange, which is called *simultaneous,* or *synchronous,* can accommodate a number of users, limited only by the number of "ports," or access, lines to the computer.

The sudden feeling of instantaneous contact that is created can be exhilarating. For instance, in our work with NOTEPAD, we have held synchronous conferences with users spread all the way from Sweden to France, Japan, Australia, all at the same time. Yet this form of contact may also be distracting or awkward. Suppose you have only 5 minutes to review past messages. Your boss enters the system and sends you a private message that says, "Hello, what did you think of the new budget?" You may wish you had never heard of synchronous communication.

On the other hand, there may be an emergency that calls for a number of people to be assembled to solve a specific problem, and an instantaneous crisis conference will save the day by enabling them to resolve the issue much faster than by any other form of communication.

What is known, then, about the special group dynamics of simultaneous message sending? What is this form of interaction good for?

Although there is less experience with synchronous conferencing than there is for electronic mail, bulletin boards, and other forms of message exchange, systematic study and practical application have combined to give us some useful information. Synchronous conferencing has proven to be eminently applicable to crisis management and decision support in organizations.

The application of this technology to the resolution of crises was first proposed at the time of the international Berlin emergency, and initial studies were conducted at the Institute for Defense Analyses and at the Rand Corporation, notably by Tom Belden and Wallace Sinaiko at IDA and by Norm Dalkey and Paul Baran at Rand. In 1972, the FORUM project, which was funded by DARPA (Defense Advanced Research Projects Agency), led to the creation of the first network-based teleconferencing system. It is on this foundation that the author and his colleagues implemented crisis simulations designed to test some of the initial concepts proposed in this field.

In 1975, an article in the February 7 issue of *Science Magazine* written by Kupperman, Wilcox, and Smith, suggested the use of computer-based conferencing "to achieve an increased level of understanding of differing value systems" and thus to assist in the resolution of crises. In a letter to the editor of *Science* (12) the

FORUM team suggested at the time that careful study of the features of teleconferencing might reveal both opportunities and grave dangers if the technique were applied without discrimination. Later experiments with both simulated and actual crises led to the same conclusion. Several tests were run and carefully monitored using the game CRISIS, developed by Garry Shirts of Simile II (see Fig. 8-1). Later, PLANET and NOTEPAD were used in commercial international conferences. All these experiments strongly supported the need for carefully designed simulations.

In the CRISIS game, six of the participants represent nations, while the other two play the roles of "Director" and "World Press." The fictitious nations vary in size and military strength. Each has goals of securing a resource of vital importance, as well as striving to preserve world order and prevent their own destruction. The game typically begins as the four largest countries (Axiom, Burymore, Camelot, and Dolchaveet) notify the Director of their decisions and actions toward the crisis situation. These decisions, made at the beginning of each of three structured periods, range from a policy of neutrality to that of committing units of armed forces to take over the Dermatium Mines where the vital resource is located. The Director notifies all countries when a session period begins and ends, and as a result of their decisions, what consequences have developed relative to the probability of war, their potential loss of office by revolution, and other related possible outcomes.

Several computer conferences were run under these conditions, and the resulting files were analyzed with the help of a special statistical program. All countries exchanged messages among themselves, some using this facility considerably more than others. Participants interacted through the private message mode to form co-

FIGURE 8-1   Map of nations for CRISIS simulation. (*Credit*: Dr. Garry Shirts.)

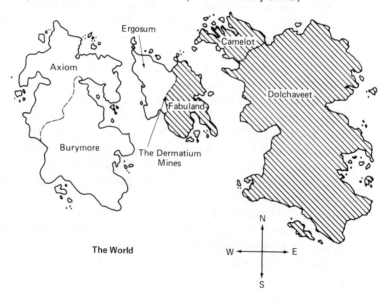

alitions, and transmitted public messages in attempts to clarify procedures or present national policy statements, which did not necessarily reflect (and often contradicted) their statements made in the private mode.

These conferences were analyzed for several parameters that determine the development of any crisis. First was *information flow*. As we have already indicated, a characteristic of group interaction during a computer conference, which is not possible with other media, is the ability for each participant to speak without restrictions. Unlike face-to-face, audio, or video interaction, in which only one person may speak at a time, computer conferencing allows each person to make statements whenever he or she desires. Theoretically, the total amount of information transferred during the conference is limited only by the typing skill of the participants and the computer terminal printing speed, as well as the ability of participants to read and process proceedings.

In our first test, using the total number of characters transmitted by the group, divided by the length of the conference (180 minutes), and assuming a word length of 5 characters, we found an information exchange rate of 67 words per minute during the conference. Since the average typing speed was only 27 words per minute for the group, it is obvious that there was a high degree of simultaneous message transmission. In an analysis of problem-solving dialogue, researcher Alphonse Chapanis has reported information exchange rates ranging between 10 and 18 words per minute (wpm) for teletype communication, 17 wpm for handwriting, 171 wpm for voice, and 190 wpm for a communications-rich environment.

Coalition behavior was another important parameter. We examined the percentage of private messages each nation sent to and received from its allies and adversaries, reflecting the two coalitions that were formed during the test. Nations of the winning coalition interacted significantly more among themselves than did losing nations (which interacted more with their adversaries).

In these CRISIS conferences there was a significantly larger number of private than public transmissions as attempts were made by each nation to solicit support from others and develop alliances and compromises. The participation map of Fig. 8-2 shows a marked difference in message-sending behavior between the three staff roles (Director, Secretary, and World Press) and the six nations. Staff activity tended to be more public, while the rectangles representing the nations clustered together in the private region.

It is of interest to review the similarities and differences between the CRISIS game as it was observed in computer conferencing and as it is known by the game designers to behave in face-to-face interaction. Dr. Shirts has reported:

> As director [of the computer simulation] I felt a great deal more control of the game than in the face-to-face mode. I felt confident that if I put something on the machine, it would be read by everyone, or if it weren't read, it would be available for them to read when they had time. I felt in closer contact. In face-to-face games, one is never sure that the verbal requests are heard, and the players have the advantage of "not hearing" in order to gain time or do what they want.

While we have not attempted controlled comparisons, Dr. Shirts notes that face-to-face groups, like computer conferencing groups, start out slowly in the inter-

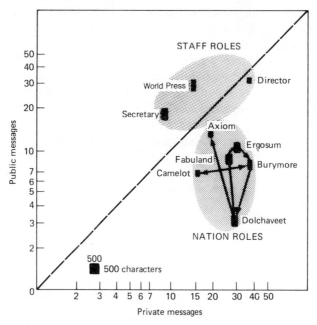

FIGURE 8-2   Participation map for CRISIS-2.

national CRISIS game, with each participant exploring possible alliances with all others, while the group is seriously attempting to find a peaceful solution. The turning point takes place when one country makes a secret suggestion for coalition to another country. Face-to-face groups discover such activity faster than do computer conferencing groups because each country's team can observe the behavior of the other players. The deterioration of trust in the computer conference takes place when someone makes the first public accusation that a secret coalition is being formed by others, or when a secret message is leaked—not unlike real-world events.

In both media, the trust level then begins to decline, coalitions form rapidly, and hard action is taken. The winning coalitions formed by our users have not been typical of the face-to-face coalitions, which usually form along historical lines. In about 90 percent of all face-to-face outcomes, such a coalition ends the game. In only a few cases does the World Organization succeed in establishing an international peace-maintaining force in the CRISIS game.

These experiments support the view that groups of people linked via computer conferencing can work together in real time, communicate a great deal of information, form coalitions, and reach momentous decisions. However, they do not indicate that the decisions are better than those of a face-to-face group. The ability of the system to carry a large quantity of information could even be used to confuse or mislead an adversary just as easily as it could be used to help or enlighten.

We must examine the behavior of the groups in more detail to understand the phenomena of conferencing.

BEHAVIOR OF SYNCHRONOUS GROUPS

As more people join a conference, many parameters of communications change. First, session length tends to increase because personal dialogue is encouraged by more correspondents being online. Figure 8-3 shows this effect very clearly.

Another parameter affected is the rate of message exchange. Public messages are stimulated. So are private messages, as long as the number of users in the discussion is less than five. After that, the frequency of private messages drops again, presumably because there is greater pressure to communicate "on the record" as a group (Fig. 8-4).

At the same time, both private and public messages get shorter (Fig. 8-5). We see the same effect in Fig. 8-6, which shows what happens to the average frequency and length of public and private messages when the single user becomes part of a live conference.

In summary, as the message system moves from a single-user situation to a live conference, the rate of message exchange goes up, and verbosity drops. The proportion of private messages is highest for two-user dialogue but decreases for larger groups. The rate of information exchange follows different patterns in the public

FIGURE 8-3   Effect of group size on session duration.

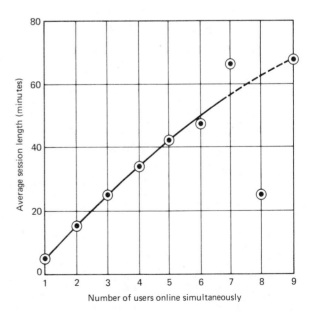

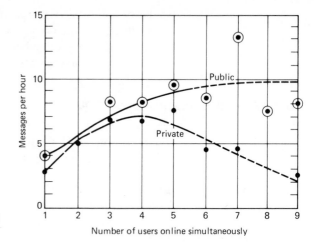

FIGURE 8-4 Effect of synchroneity on the rate of message exchange.

and in the private mode. The number of messages per hour doubles as one moves from single-user situations to groups with three or four users. As the group gets even larger, however, the rate of private message exchange decreases. When seven or eight users are online, the number of private messages sent per hour is no higher than it was for a single user.

Another curious fact of synchronous communication emerges when live conferences are compared with single-user situations in terms of participation rates. The

FIGURE 8-5 Effect of group size on verbosity.

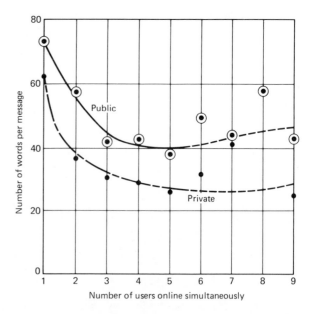

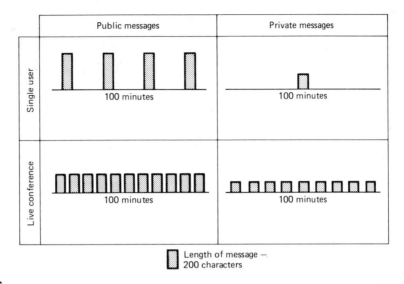

FIGURE 8-6

distribution of participation in a live conference is best described by a linear function (straight line). Participation in asynchronous groups, which usually involves a single user at a time, is best described by the exponential decrease we have seen earlier. One interpretation of this difference is that live conferencing may promote equality of participation by drawing out people who tend to remain quiet in face-to-face meetings and in electronic mail (Figs. 8-7 and 8-8).

COMPUTER CONFERENCING AND DECISION SUPPORT

These statistical results, coupled with the observations of crisis management tests mentioned earlier, support the opinion often expressed by skilled users of message systems. Proper training is essential *before* an emergency. The technology represents only a tool. Its use in ordinary situations teaches us nothing about its application when time is of the essence, tempers flare up, and all the participants feel overloaded with information as trust plummets.

The need for careful attention to the human factors of communications culminates in the design of message systems for decision support and in the actual construction of decision centers. Infomedia Corporation created such a center for its own use, based on its knowledge of computer conferencing. The facility is shown in Fig. 8-9. This was the first facility specifically designed around a computer conferencing system.

The purpose of the decision center goes beyond crisis resolution. Its goal is to enhance the quality of decisions made by the organization. Much of the time these

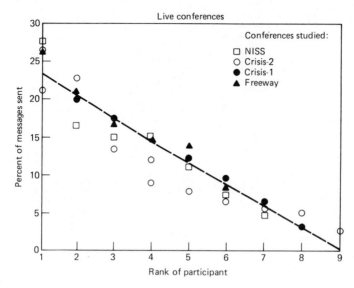

FIGURE 8-7

FIGURE 8-8

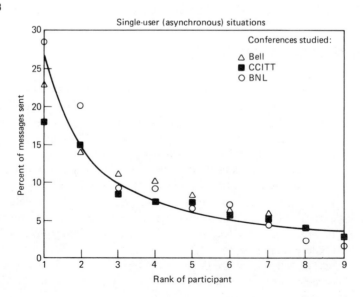

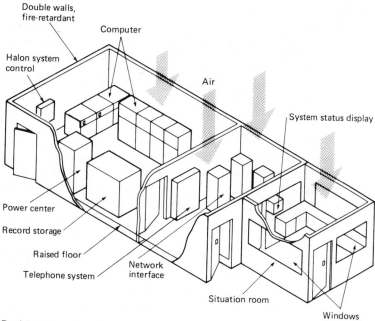

FIGURE 8-9   Decision support center.

decisions are made at remote locations linked by the message system. However, there are at least four conditions under which a face-to-face meeting in a specially designed room is of particular importance. These conditions are:

1 Problem Solving

Two or more individuals meet to examine documents or review data in the context of a larger process of group interaction. The other participants are at remote sites and use the message system to communicate, either in real time or in delayed time with the people at the center. The process may involve modeling, planning, forecasting, or business decision making, and may last from a few hours to several weeks.

2 Process Analysis and Integration

A complex operation in progress at a remote site requires continual management attention and careful recording of key actions taken. Various models may be involved, and several points of view need to be integrated. Examples of this situation include engineering management and some negotiation meetings.

3 Information Control

A group assembled in the situation room is seeking to gather information from remote resources. This may involve synchronous conferencing displayed on large monitors and telephone interaction with the participants. This process will generally use such computer-based tools to poll group members and aggregate their judgment in graphic form.

4 Crisis Management

In an emergency a large, complex process loaded with emotional issues may have to be controlled from a single room serving as the "information fusion point." Accordingly, this "situation room" must be easily convertible into a crisis center where all essential information can be centralized in a form which is easily understandable in its context, magnitude, and relevance to the emergency at hand.

To support these various types of group interaction, one should study the alternative ways in which special telephone circuits can be made available. The situation room should be equipped with an audioconferencing facility independent of the main telephone switch. It should use redundant electrical circuits and air conditioners. A fault-tolerant computer with redundant network access, direct lines bypassing the network, and even satellite access, and independent power are obvious requirements if the center has an operational responsibility.

The size of a situation room will vary depending on the type of application and expected group size. A large room is advisable if extensive audio- and videoconferencing is contemplated. In that case the walls should not be parallel, depending on the specific equipment selected and on acoustic requirements.

Conversion of such a room to videoconferencing would simply involve placement of additional monitors and controls. Cameras may be located in the adjacent room, to shoot through glass partitions. Factors we also consider in such situations include availability of drapes, special lighting, and design of controls. Although not directly related to the features of the computer message system, they are important human factors of its environment and hence of its successful application.

The contribution that the emergency management community can expect from the new information technology of message systems will come not from better or faster computers, but from greater understanding of group dynamics in crisis situations, a greater ability to prepare for such situations through sophisticated simulations and training, and from a finer analysis of their qualitative and quantitative characteristics.

Our ability to install computers and build communications channels far exceeds our understanding of decision-making behavior under stress conditions. Our knowledge of programming and engineering outweighs our grasp of the human and organizational factors that foster creativity. It is a fact of life that, by their very nature, good information systems tend to attract crises. Good message systems follow the same rule.

Case Study 8: From Three Mile Island to Diablo Canyon

Emergencies are characterized by an increase in information flow, an explosion in the topological complexity of the information network, and a feeling of intense psychological pressure among the participants. This means that many people and organizations who should be talking to each other do not do so until communication is forced upon them by an external emergency. The group members often find themselves confronted with unfamiliar procedures and with unknown partners in the crisis management process, and decisions have to be made under conditions of low group trust and inadequate information content.

Although such communications crises are familiar on the federal, state, and local government levels, they are also familiar in private industry. The nuclear accident at Three Mile Island (TMI) is a case in point. Given that the trigger for the accident was a physical malfunction, the real crisis was in many ways a crisis of communications. Plant operators and company personnel did not have access to outside experts who might have brought essential information to the discussion. There was a low level of trust between personnel in the industry and government officials, and it quickly became impossible to obtain accurate and reliable data about the situation because antagonism between industry and the press introduced into the perception of the crisis a third component whose role had not been anticipated: namely, a misunderstanding of that information which was in fact communicated. There were obvious linguistic and cultural differences between the three communities involved. These differences were exacerbated by lack of an effective communications tool.

One of the responses to the TMI emergency was the creation of a computer conferencing network called "NUCLEAR NOTEPAD," dedicated to preventing future accidents through the exchange of nuclear safety information within the industry. This system now links together 64 companies that own 72 nuclear power plants. It also ties the United States with 12 foreign utilities, including France, Japan, Italy, Sweden, Spain, Taiwan, and Canada. NUCLEAR NOTEPAD gives the affected utility access to outside resources and provides timely, accurate information to the community at large. The structure of the computer conference used during an emergency is shown in Fig. 8-10. The "Hotline" is an activity in which the affected utility company controls all information. Unless requested, no other utility transmits messages in this conference. All other communications related to the crisis are placed into the "Emergency Planners Information Exchange" activity. The use of NUCLEAR NOTEPAD during an actual emergency (namely, the incident at the Crystal River nuclear plant on February 26, 1980) has been described as follows by an industry publication, illustrating the key role played by the computer:

> A series of events had begun at 2:23 p.m. that were to bring about the emergency shutdown of Crystal River 3, a 797 pressurized water reactor that had come into commercial operation three years earlier. This was of particular interest to Randy Pack because his job, heading INPO's Criteria Development and Analysis Division, is to assemble the evaluation teams which—in the wake of the accident at Three Mile Island—are

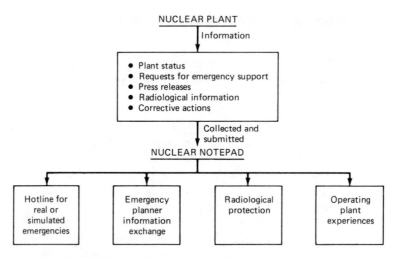

NUCLEAR PLANT

Information

- Plant status
- Requests for emergency support
- Press releases
- Radiological information
- Corrective actions

Collected and submitted

NUCLEAR NOTEPAD

| Hotline for real or simulated emergencies | Emergency planner information exchange | Radiological protection | Operating plant experiences |

FIGURE 8-10   Structure of NOTEPAD activities in a nuclear plant emergency.

studying and making recommendations on the operating procedures at all utility-owned reactors in the United States.

The Crystal River events also concerned his former colleagues at Palo Alto, in particular the year-old Nuclear Safety Analysis Center (NSAC).

At 5:49 p.m. (2:49 p.m. Pacific time), Pack sent out an appeal over the NOTEPAD system:

> "Does anyone have information on the incident at Crystal River this afternoon? I would like any news immediately."

It was not long before Pack was brought into the picture on Crystal River, and it was not long before NSAC's director, Edwin L. Zebroski (now at INPO in Atlanta), was arranging that continual updates be transmitted via NOTEPAD to members around the country. One of the earliest messages:

> "Continuation of Crystal River. NRC team is on site; NSAC and INPO teams in communication with plant. P. Baynard of Florida Power will update or revise this information as needed."

(Patsy Baynard is manager of the nuclear support system at Florida Power.)

As it turned out, a power failure in the non-nuclear instrumentation at Crystal River led to a brief emergency shutdown: 43,000 gallons of radioactive water were spilled into the containment as operators deliberately prolonged the high-pressure injection system to ensure adequate cooling.

Comparing NOTEPAD to other media in a brief for the White House in the spring of 1980, Dr. Zebroski remarked:

More than 100 NOTEPAD stations are now in operation, most of them in utilities. Each one consists of a computer terminal and printer.

NOTEPAD is used for rapid transmittal of information about events in plants and requests for information. Voice communication by telephone is also used but is less convenient for transmitting numerical information or for communicating the same information rapidly to a group of recipients. . . .

On August 19, 1981, we observed the use of NUCLEAR NOTEPAD in the management of another nuclear emergency. The crisis, however, was not an actual accident, but a drill organized by Pacific Gas and Electric Company (PG&E) in San Francisco. It involved a hypothetical equipment malfunction at the Diablo Canyon nuclear plant, consisting of the ejection of a rod from the reactor housing, a fire in the switch gear room, and loss of transmission power to the plant.

The computer conference dealing with this simulated emergency began at 8:28 A.M., and lasted 8 hours. It was used by the decision makers who would be involved in a real crisis, including the Emergency Operations Facility team at PG&E, the Diablo Canyon nuclear plant, and members of the Corporate Emergency Response Plan. The drill was designed to test PG&E's emergency communication procedures and was required by the Nuclear Regulatory Commission as part of the licensing process.

During a period of 8 hours NUCLEAR NOTEPAD was used for rapid dissemination of statements regarding plant status, radiological release, corrective actions, and evacuation procedures. Involved in the crisis network were the Corporate Incident Response Center, the Governmental and Public Affairs offices, media centers, the news bureau, the rumor control center, and the Santa Maria office of PG&E. The Institute of Nuclear Power Operations (located in Atlanta, Georgia) was also given access to the activity, since in a real emergency INPO would monitor the situation and offer the assistance of its own experts (Fig. 8-11).

In designing its emergency response plan, PG&E viewed NOTEPAD as a communication medium whose unique features would allow PG&E to significantly augment and improve its existing communications capabilities (namely, voice, radio, and data). Specifically, PG&E recognized that with the system it could:

- Create a single historical record of events, easily retrievable at any time
- Simultaneously transmit information to concerned PG&E officials
- Draw in outside expertise as needed

For PG&E, these combined features served two very important functions. They guarded against distortion of events and subsequent rumors—(everyone has the same facts at the same time)—and obviated the flood of distracting phone calls to the Emergency Operations Facility. Voice communications to transmit these items are not impossible, but dictation of important statements and timely news releases is time-consuming on both ends and subject to error.

Statistics gathered on the drill indicated that in the 8-hour period PG&E sent 36 *public* messages and 148 *private* messages. Thus, each participant received an average of 51 messages. The fact that four times as many private messages as public were sent strongly underlined the importance of having access to private

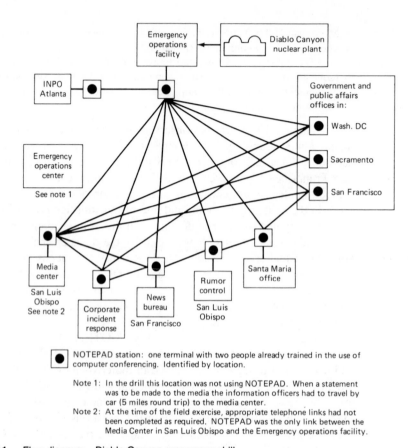

NOTEPAD station: one terminal with two people already trained in the use of computer conferencing. Identified by location.

Note 1: In the drill this location was not using NOTEPAD. When a statement was to be made to the media the information officers had to travel by car (5 miles round trip) to the media center.

Note 2: At the time of the field exercise, appropriate telephone links had not been completed as required. NOTEPAD was the only link between the Media Center in San Luis Obispo and the Emergency operations facility.

FIGURE 8-11   Flow diagram—Diablo Canyon emergency drill.

channels for problem solving, questions, or any other type of communications that is more appropriately directed to an individual than to the whole group.

Following the drill, Paul Girard (a Public Information Representative at PG&E) remarked that "NOTEPAD allowed us to overcome many of the communications barriers that might be encountered during an emergency." Along this line, he pointed out that NOTEPAD was the only communications link between the media center in San Luis Obispo and the Emergency Operations Facility during the field exercise, because appropriate telephone links had not been completed as required.

The success of PG&E's field exercise on August 19 clearly demonstrated that NOTEPAD effectively tied together company experts and decision makers, and facilitated their responsibility to present well-informed responses to government authorities, the press, and the public (see Fig. 8-12).

The analysis of NOTEPAD activities enables us to bring to such a crisis a level of quantification not generally available. And this ability in turn opens the door to a rich avenue of future R&D for the classification and management of crises. For instance, we can rank participants according to their use of specific system commands. These statistics provide a measure of the effectiveness of the system training and help us understand information needs better at specific points in the network. They also emphasize the great need felt by participants for retrieval of earlier statements (example: "What exactly did the NRC say about emergency plans this morning?"), and for an accurate update of the list of group members at any given time.

Such functions cannot be provided at all under other media, whether they are voice-based like audioconferencing or text-based like Telex or TWX. Analyzing the emergency conference, researcher Jennifer O'Radnik found that the average length of entries made during the drill was 143 words, much higher than private notes (33 words). This reflects the nature of the public entries, which usually were press releases. There were four times as many private as public messages, indicating a rapid exchange of short questions and requests.

The Emergency Operations Facility was responsible for 80 percent of the public

FIGURE 8-12   Typical NOTEPAD transcript during PG&E drill.

```
ACTION: Status (of Participant) All

The Title of Activity 2006 is:
EMERGENCY COMMUNICATIONS/DIABLO CANYON AUGUST 19, 1981

       Name            Last Time Entered         Last Entry Seen
Girard (Paul)          Present                         4
EOF (PG&E)             Present                         4
EOC (County)           Never entered
CIRC (PG&E)            Present                         4
NBSF (PG&E)            Present                         4
MCSLO (PG&E)           Present                         4
GPASACTO (PG&E)        Present                         4
GPASF (PF&E)           19-AUG-81   9:23 AM             4
GPADC (PG&E)           Present                         4
RUMOR (PG&E)           Present                         4
SMARIA (PG&E)          Present                         4
Lear (Jennifer)        Present                         4
INPO (Atlanta)         19-AUG-81   8:48 AM             4

ACTION:

Now Typing: EOF (PG&E)

[13] EOF (PG&E)
This is a drill!!!  GSP
       THE STATE OFFICE OF EMERGENCY SERVICES HAS REQUESTED
ASSISTANCE FROM THE FEDERAL DEPARTMENT OF ENERGY FOR
RADIOLOGICAL ASSESSMENT OF AIRBORNE RELEASES, THE
DEPARTMENT OF ENERGY ACTIVATED ITS ATMOSPHERIC RELEASE
ADVISORY CAPABILITY (A.R.A.C.) COMPUTERIZED DOSE ASSESSMENT
SYSTEM AND DISPATCHED A HELICOPTER WITH RADIATION
MONITORING INSTRUMENTS FROM ITS LAS VEGAS FACILITY. THE
ESTIMATED TIME OF ARRIVAL OF THE HELICOPTER IS 1:00 PM. this is
a drill!!!  THE FOLLOWING IS THE LATEST PRESS RELEASE FROM THE
COUNTY. GSP

Now Joining: INPO (Drill)
```

messages and only 23 percent of the private ones. This reflects its role as the official broadcaster of information.

To our knowledge the PG&E field exercise of August 19, 1981, represents the first time that computer conferencing was used for public information response in connection with a simulated industrial crisis.

The lessons drawn from the activities we have mentioned are clear: The use of computer conferencing during a crisis provides a powerful, adaptable framework. *But*, like any other information technology, it demands adequate training and careful professional facilitation. One simply cannot afford to improvise, relying on the computer to sort out relevant information from trivia in the heat of an actual emergency. Even the appropriate structure to be used during a crisis is a matter of careful selection and varies with the nature of the organizations involved. And it is wise to keep in mind that the long-term impact of conferencing techniques on management styles and on informal networks is unknown.

## CHAPTER 9

TOMORROW: MESSAGE SYSTEMS ON PUBLIC NETWORKS

BULLETIN BOARDS AND ELECTRONIC NEWSPAPERS

Spurred by the rapid dissemination of personal computers with sizable mass storage, hundreds of "bulletin boards" are springing up across the United States. They are implemented on personal computers such as the Apple or the IBM PC, which their owners place on the telephone network by installing a special line. Any user with a home terminal of practically any price or type can call and post messages on the "board." Users need only the board's telephone number and a little patience, since the message center can accommodate only one user at a time. Some specialized journals publish such phone numbers, and each bulletin board generally provides a directory of other similar centers, so that an enterprising user can easily get his or her own list of message systems that covers the whole country.

The command structure of these systems is quite simple. They typically allow a user to type a single letter, to review past messages, to browse through the entire list of messages, to enter a new message, and so on. Luxuries such as key words or sublists of participants are generally not provided.

Applications of these bulletin boards range from astronomy and political issues to pornography and special clubs with interests in home computers or rocketry. Anyone with a terminal device can enter these groups, so that no way exists to verify the identity of one's correspondents. And these services are free, for the same reason.

FIGURE 9-1   Entering a publicly available "bulletin board."

```
================================
DATATECH BBS AND ROP/M SYSTEM
================================

SYSTEM HOURS –>    MONDAY–SUNDAY 8PM–8AM
       PACIFIC     OTHER TIMES WHEN THE SYSTEM IS
       TIME        NOT BEING USED FOR BUSINESS

LOGIN VERSION 2.3B (1.2)

DATATECH COMPUTER SERVICES
NODE 006 SAN FRANCISCO, CALIF

USERID (C/R IF NONE)  :069324

YOU HAVE CALLED 1 TIMES
YOU WERE LAST ON 09/26/82
LOGGING JIMMY FLOYD AT 16:47:31 10/11/82

DATATECH BBS VERSION 2.6

TYPE B FOR BULLETINS/NEWS
TYPE I FOR INFORMATION
TYPE ? FOR HELP

ACTIVE # OF MSG'S 17
YOU ARE CALLER # 434
NEXT MSG # WILL BE 41
LAST MESSAGE READ 0

SORRY, NO NEW MAIL FOR YOU TODAY

B,E,R,H,S,K,G,I,C,M,J,U,P,X,F,N,O,Q,Z,L,T,#,RP,RS,RF,CHAT,? FOR HELP
```

```
COMMAND:?

FUNCTIONS SUPPORTED:
USE CTL-K TO ABORT, CTL-S TO PAUSE.

B  .  = PRINT BULLETINS
C     = UPPER/LOWER CASE TOGGLE
E     = ENTER MESSAGE
F     = LINE FEED TOGGLE
G     = GOODBYE (LEAVE SYSTEM)
H     = PRINT HELP FILE
I     = SYSTEM INFORMATION
K     = KILL MESSAGE
L     = LIST OF USERS
M     = MESSAGE ALERT (MSG FOR YOU?)
N     = SET NULLS
O     = OTHER SYSTEMS LIST
P     = BELL TOGGLE
Q     = QUICK SUMMARY
R     = RETRIEVE MESSAGE
RF    = RETRIEVE WITH MORE PAUSE AFTER EACH MSG
RP    = RETRIEVE ALL NEW MSGS WITH PROMPTING
RS    = RETRIEVE WITH PROMPTING (SUPERB)
S     = SUMMARY
T     = TIME/DATE/CONNECT TIME
U     = SET USER PARMS/CHANGE PASSWORD
X     = EXPERT TOGGLE
Z     = CONTINUE MES ENTRY AFTER ALERT
?     = PRINT THIS MENU
#     = MESSAGES IN SYSTEM
CHAT  = CHAT WITH SYSOP

COMMANDS MAY BE STRUNG TOGETHER, SEPARATED BY SEMICOLONS.
FOR EXAMPLE, /R;123/ RETRIEVES MESSAGE # 123.
TO RETRIEVE A SEQUENCE OF MESSAGES FROM A STARTING
POINT TO THE END,APPEND A + TO THE MSG NUMBER
FOR EXAMPLE,TO SEE ALL MSGS FROM #1 TO THE END
YOU WOULD DO  R;1+ (RETURN)
FOR MORE HELP AND HINTS/TIPS ON USAGE,USE THE H COMMAND

B,E,R,H,S,K,G,I,O,M,J,U,P,X,F,N,O,Q,Z,L,T,#,RP,RS,RF,CHAT,? FOR HELP

COMMAND:R;1+

USE CTL-K TO ABORT, CTL-S TO PAUSE.
TYPE CONTROL-N TO SKIP TO NEXT MSG.
```

FIGURE 9-2   Entering a bulletin board system: list of all available functions.

Less colorful but operating at a higher level of sophistication are systems such as the Source or CompuServe, which offer various modes of electronic message exchange. Here the user is charged not only for access time (which can vary depending on transmission speed and time of day), but also for characters sent and received, and for storage. Although such services generally call themselves "Videotex," they are simply offering access to a timesharing system where the user can run either database consultation programs or electronic mail. Among the popular features of the system are *The New York Times* database and the Dow-Jones stock quotes. The electronic message exchange is mostly centered on the type of mailbox service which evolved first around ARPANET 10 years ago.

```
MSG # 2 09/20/82 19:49:36 FROM: DAVE LENKER
SUBJECT: HELLO TO: ALL USERS

FROM SACRAMENTO....H8 ON LINE 5:00PM — 9:00 PM
WOULD BE HAPPY TO CHAT OR LEAVE MESSAGE FOR 018DTLH8
WILL HAVE ERROR—FREE DATA TRANSFER BY 01 OCTOBER
CALL 916—423—3389 FOR CHAT
DAVE
```

```
MSG # 3 09/21/82 02:32:38 FROM: AMADEUS AMADEUS
SUBJECT: DU.COM &.DOC TO: ALL CP/MERS

WHILE THIS IS AN RCPM YOU MITE LIKE THIS DISK UTILITY. LOOK AT
ANY PART OF THE FLOOPY. THE DIRECTORY— SYSTEM ETC. UNERA
FILES A GIFT FROM WARD CHRISTIANSON TO THE PEOPLE..CP/M'S DISK
DOCTOR! IF YOU HAVE MODEM? YOU KNOW HOW TO RETRIEVE THIS.
IF YOU DON'T LEAVE A MESSAGE FOR THE SYSOP..
```

```
MSG # 21 10/01/82 01:00:28 FROM: KENNY JACK
SUBJECT: VIC USER TO: ALL

I AM A NEW COMPUTER USER I HAVE
A COMMODORE VIC—20 AND I AM WONDERING IF
ANY ONE HAS ANY INFO ON THE VIC—20
I AM ALSO LOOKING FOR SOME PHONE NUMBERS
TO OTHER BBS IN OAKLAND,BERKLEY AND SF
IF ANYONE CAN GIVE ME ANY INFO JUST LEAVE ME A MESSAGE
!
!
!
```

THANKS KENNY JACK

FIGURE 9-3 Entering a bulletin board system: three messages are displayed.

Since many computer message systems and databases share certain characteristics (similar access and similar ways to set key words and to retrieve by date or author), it is logical to combine them and create electronic "newspapers." Users can subscribe to such a newspaper by placing their names on a distribution list. They will be notified about new information every time they log in, and will be able to get items of interest displayed by title, summary, or full text.

We may think of an electronic newspaper as a number of computer conferences proceeding in parallel: Each conference has an organizer who is the editor-in-chief controlling circulation, a small group of contributors who submit articles or news items, and a large number of readers recognized by the system as observers. At the discretion of the organizer, they may or may not be able to send private messages to each other, but they cannot write entries on the public record. Finally, each conference includes one or two editors who can delete or change the text of the entries on the public record. One example of such an application, the LINC service at Loughborough in England, is given in Case Study 9.

THE DREAM OF VIDEOTEX

Whenever the terms *Teletext* (with a "T" at the end) and *Videotex* (no such "T") are introduced, it is customary to define them. *Teletext* is the broadcast of information pages selected by the decoder of an individual subscriber, picking what he or she wants out of the television channel. *Videotext* is a more sophisticated service which is interactive in nature, the user having the ability to access the central database directly through his or her telephone or through a two-way cable system. Based on this rough definition, Videotex is the medium of greatest interest to us in terms of message systems.

The confusion in terminology in this new industry is clearly deliberate. Some companies which offer classical timesharing services are marketing them as Videotex, and this is seen as a heresy by many business and technical people, who argue that Videotex means television (as opposed to terminals or computers) and graphics in color (as opposed to black and white text). Unfortunately, this definition would disqualify not only the current versions of the Source and CompuServe, but most of the services that are grouping themselves under the Videotex label. These timesharing services, on the other hand, offer much more power than most Videotex products. What they lack in color graphics they make up in the ability to provide user interaction, and especially electronic mailboxes, as we have seen earlier. But wait! Some hybrids of Teletext can be made interactive too. And Teletext has all the colors of Videotex, uses television, and can be very inexpensive. One medium is based on the broadcasting of thousands of information "frames," among which the user selects what he or she wants, guided by a "menu"; the other is computer-controlled interaction through a user keyboard. But both approaches allow the creation of hybrids.

All this simply means is that there are many ways to skin a cat—or a confused customer. There are also many bright engineers in the business capable of solving the problem of information delivery in many different ways for which no labels are as yet adequate.

All we can say is that a family of new electronic systems giving the public wide access to stored information is now in the design stage and will probably make an impact on public communications in years to come. The motivation for developing these systems, which are called *Prestel, Titan, Teletel, Telidon, Antiope*, etc., comes from:

1 *The realization that in developed countries the electronics industry will face major unemployment problems unless a new wave of communications products is scheduled for introduction in the 1980s and 1990s.* Classical telephone deployment has reached saturation in the western world, and the supply of phone networks to the third world, although a lucrative market, has become a competitive jungle. In France, for example, the Ministry of Industry estimates that thousands of qualified technicians will be out of work and will become an economic burden to the nation unless the massive telephone effort of the 1960s and 1970s is followed through very soon.

2 *The dramatic decrease in hardware costs for computer technology.* This trend makes it possible to envision large digital storage facilities at every television station and keyboard terminal in a significant percentage of homes. The British Prestel system has developed two types of home or office terminals. The French PTT has launched a project to replace home telephone sets with keyboard terminals, allowing, as a first step, searches of the subscriber directory. Unlimited applications can be introduced once the subscriber has access to a keyboard rather than a simple telephone dial.

3 *The evolving structure and increasing sophistication of commercial markets, requiring customers to make complex decisions on the basis of stock market quotations, commodity price tables, airline reservation schedules, library catalogs, and many other types of structured data.* To the extent that such data can be reduced to single frames or pages and displayed on home monitors, an enormous information market can be created. It offers unlimited opportunities to advertisers as well as to other industries (although it may also have a severe adverse impact on some commercial sectors).

Given these three motivations, which seem to combine to make Teletext/Videotex systems an almost irresistible economic necessity, two questions are unavoidable: First, what are the technical limitations inherent in the concept of information "pages"; and second, what are the social and individual human factors that may slow down the introduction of the technology?

These questions are important because we have already experienced three major instances of economic areas that have been slow to reach their projected potential because of such factors. Computer-aided instruction, which was based on an information technology very similar to Teletext, has experienced delays. Cable television ("the wired nation") has not grown according to the projections of the 1960s. And office automation, while it is developing rapidly at the hardware level, is being severely constrained by human structures in the office and by behavioral "driving functions" in the marketplace.

Reviewing the state of Teletext and public broadcasting in April 1980, John Carey and his colleagues at the Alternate Media Center of New York University listed six possible providers of future services. They are:

1 The cable television industry, which has excess capacity in its channels, can charge on a page basis, and has few regulatory limitations.

2 Broadcast networks, which can provide nationwide coverage but have concerns about loss of advertising revenue from their regular programming.

3 Independent stations, which have good knowledge of their local audience but also have an uncertain economic motivation and poor access to capital.

4 Public broadcasting, which has an ideal position to serve the public with better information services but lacks financial resources to support innovation.

5 Newspapers and news services, which are "well-placed to provide diversified information services" (but may be concerned with a change in their working culture, which is still oriented to the printed page).

6 Private entrepreneurs and information providers.

The report points out that alliances and partnerships are likely to form between these groups, ad agencies, banks, and large retailers. To the extent that the service can be made interactive, these systems will be an ideal support for electronic mail and computer conferencing. This view is supported by other experts. For example, in an article summarizing the "service and system implications" of the technology (13), Mike Noll has pointed out that:

> Electronic banking, teleshopping, electronic mail, and specialized information retrieval are services that would appeal to the consumer because of their time and money-saving potential and possibilities for increasing personal efficiency—in essence, utility. These services would enable consumers to manage their households better and keep in contact with family members and friends. From a consumer positioning viewpoint, these services appear to be part of the home communications and work center. These would be truly telecommunications—a textual adjunct to voice telephony.

And yet when it comes to message systems, the apparent promise of Videotex has remained simply that: a promise. Even simple electronic mail has played only a small role in large-scale experiments such as the Teletel field trial involving thousands of French homes, and in the similar Florida test sponsored jointly by AT&T and the Knight-Ridder newspaper chain.

This failure for public communications to develop through the technology can be interpreted in various ways. Providing enough ports into a central computer to accommodate hundreds of simultaneous users remains a tricky challenge. If the number of ports is too small, users have to queue up, which is discouraging. This is true with respect to professional timesharing users, but becomes devastating in the case of a public service—one that has to compete for the TV screen with such formidable competitors as Bugs Bunny and "As the World Turns." If the central computer is powerful and the communications interface massive enough to provide instant response, the cost of the system becomes prohibitive. Companies that offer this type of service need strong backing to stay in business and usually end up as part of a larger empire. Thus, the Source is linked to *Reader's Digest,* CompuServe belongs to H&R Block, and Dialcom belongs to ITT.

This lack of public enthusiasm for message systems may also come from other reasons, however. One of these reasons has to be the complexity of the systems themselves. In spite of all the talk about systems being "user-friendly," the public has never really had an opportunity to see a system that was stripped of computer jargon. Even the mailbox services are too hard to access and use. Another reason may be that the timing is still wrong. Computer message systems are a new medium for communications. Experience with them has to start gradually, and it has to spread through business and industrial applications, where they are clearly cost-justified, before making a public impact. And when that happens, we don't know if the public impact will be as a result of television broadcasting or home computers or a combination of both. The rapid deployment of Commodore, Apple, Radio Shack, and IBM computers in homes during 1981 and 1982 has certainly taken the Videotex industry by surprise, catching it with a technology that is both obsolete and too far-fetched to merge gracefully into the home computer movement. New services and technologies will surely address this problem, but they have not appeared yet.

**In a few
years' time**
every home now equipped with a television set
and a telephone may also have:
— a VTR
— a home computer
— a teleprinter

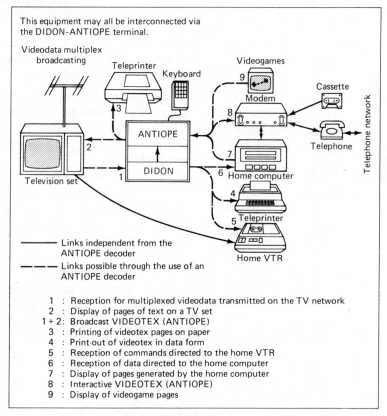

FIGURE 9-4 In a few years' time . . . (*An extract from a Videotex marketing brochure.*)

Finally, some specialists (including those close to the large-scale public trials in Europe and the United States) are saying that the failure of electronic mail to develop quickly through Videotex has a more simple and sinister reason. Perhaps those who provide the service are systematically discouraging electronic mail because they do not know how to control it. There would be several ways to do this. The most effective is to design the terminal in such a way as to discourage typing— for example, by providing a keyboard where the keys are too small or too close together to allow for convenient text entry. Another way is simply to discontinue the service or to make access to it very inconvenient, which was the case in some French public tests.

The reasons large institutions might want to discourage the public spread of electronic mail may again be multiple. They may feel that it is premature; they may fear the loss of control that would follow; or they may simply feel that other forms of access are more desirable because they are more profitable. The user who goes into the system to look up tables of baseball game results, for example, or a stock quotation, is much easier to service than a user who enters a sophisticated electronic conferencing service to argue with invisible penpals the world over about the future of humankind or the price of bread.

Never before has there been a medium of communications designed to support group interaction. Computer-based message systems have no precedent in history. All other forms of interaction are either point-to-point, such as mail, telephone, or video teleconferencing; or they involve face-to-face communications and human speech, a medium which is pleasant but often unreliable, tedious, and tricky because it is subject to misunderstandings and poor recall. Also, it demands long and costly travel to a central meeting place. Face-to-face communications tend to be dominated by the organizers and do not encourage horizontal participation.

In spite of current problems with the technology and its marketing, computer message systems will eventually develop through Videotex. It seems likely that appropriate structures will evolve to control the cost-effective development of information services to the home. Public impact promises to be very great, and issues raised by these new services will be of comparable magnitude.

PUBLIC NETWORKS: THE ISSUES

Throughout this book we have encountered a number of underlying ideas: First, the idea that the computer, with its ability for memory and logic, provides the opportunity to create a revolutionary medium for group communication. Second, the idea that this medium offers a new freedom from the constraints of time and space, making it especially well-suited to the needs of project management within and across organizations. It is also well-suited to the creation of wide horizontal links among peers, whether in lobby groups, information networks, common interest groups, research teams, or professional institutions. Third, the idea that the technology itself is only a small part of the overall medium. New roles have to be defined, a new behavior has to be acquired by users, a way to support and maintain the service has to be found, and a billing and marketing structure has to be instituted. We are beginning to understand how to achieve all this in an industrial or business setting.

Can the public at large benefit from the same improvements in communications? The previous pages have summarized some of the opportunities and concerns of the emerging Videotex field, which represents an attempt to channel into the home the type of information that has only been available previously to users of large systems. Let us assume that the problems we have evoked—the confusion of technological gadgetry, the regulatory jungle, the conflicts of interest within the service organizations themselves—can all be resolved. What form could a public message system take, and what general issues would it raise?

To stay at a very practical level, let us characterize the early user of the system.

According to industry projections, this person is probably well-educated, lives in a suburb, and has a stable job as a middle manager in a corporation. The user has a family and uses computers at work. The house contains two telephone lines, two television sets, and a personal computer. Market researchers see this person as information-hungry, with money and leisure time available, although with some feeling of time pressure. The user sees the information system as something that will make life easier, not as an added complication. He or she is a prime candidate for the use of a computer message system. First, the user may subscribe to a service that provides access to correspondence courses. He or she may join various interest groups, a bulletin board that includes political subjects and local news. Next, the user may use the system to look at want ads, and to send mail to friends across town.

If we follow this scenario, an environment is created for the widespread exchange of information throughout society on a scale we can only dream about. We are back in the days of Nicolas Tesla and Edison, when the supply of electric power to the home was beginning to be viewed as a serious possibility rather than the pipe dream of a few laboratory visionaries.

The electrical network has grown, thanks to good standardization, and it has promoted the development of a host of public utilities which buy and sell electricity to each other. In turn, these utilities have made it possible for a giant industry to grow by making and selling appliances.

The growth of the new information industry may not be so simple. There are at least three sets of issues to be overcome: some at the level of the technology, some at the level of the service, and some at the social level. The social issues are beyond the scope of this book. They have to do with the evolution of control in a system that would permit instant voting, invisible networks, and the unchecked dissemination of rumors at an unprecedented level. Another problem is that of displacement of those professions traditionally associated with the supply of information. The U.S. postal service is a prime example, since existing electronic mail systems are already capable of carrying routine first-class mail at a fraction of the price of a stamp. Yet the postal service employs about 1 percent of the U.S. labor force, and most of its revenue comes from first-class mail.

Technological issues do not stop when agreement is reached on the general outlines of access and information exchange protocols. If the service is offered through cables, it can reach only about 20 percent of American homes; only 6 percent, if an interactive system (such as electronic mail) is considered. The cost of installing cable TV is at least $500 to $600 per home, and the TV set has to be altered to serve as a terminal, with the addition of a decoder, a keyboard, and a printer interface.

It would be far easier to start from the home computer and expand its capabilities to tap into a message system through the telephone. The problem is that the phone system is not designed to handle that much traffic. Any service that requires long sessions will be costly, and any service that provides high speed to cut down on session length will demand a quality of phone service that will develop only gradually. The simple and friendly concept of the "Global Village," in other words, will need a communications infrastructure that will be closer to Mission Control at NASA or the NORAD headquarters at Cheyenne Mountain than any village the world has ever seen. The utopian view of an egalitarian flow of information may give way to a more realistic, less exciting interlocking of many incompatible services with many levels of control.

Still considering the technological issues, the nature of the signal to be carried into the home is an interesting Pandora's box that many information providers would rather not open.

Everyone in the electronic communications field is excited to the point of inebriation by the amazing progress made by technology. Computers the size of a matchbox can now effectively process text and control access to information networks. They have made technically possible the offering of powerful computer message tools at the level of every home user in the country. It will be possible to log in, to receive new text, to search according to key words, and to send new messages to any group the user wishes.

But it would be naive to assume that the technology is going to stop there and give us time to refine our software to take full advantage of these text-based systems. The next generation of communications controllers is designed to carry voice as well as data, both in digital form. Word recognition is already here, and language understanding is not very far away. Graphics and music may be part of future message systems. Our first illustration in this book was a mosaic of technical capabilities. It clearly showed that computer message systems are being swept along by successive waves of technological advances that make it very difficult to set intelligent standards or agree on ways to evaluate these new tools. Baselines disappear like sand castles at high tide.

The service issues are equally interesting. They tend to hide behind technological or business questions, because they are not easily quantified. Yet they constitute the real core of the problem.

One of the most interesting issues is: What makes us think that a global message system, even combined with excellent access to databases, can effectively compete with Bugs Bunny on a television screen, or with Donkey Kong on a video computer display? Television is a medium that provides live coverage, color, motion, sound, and high image quality. Message systems and data retrieval involve lines of text, little need for color, no motion, no sound, and a low level of graphic quality. The match between message systems and the medium of television is not obvious. A paper printer might be more effective. Once again, we seem to reach an impasse between our need for cheap and easy access, which throws us into broadcast television supplemented with a phone line, and our need for precision, memory, and logic, which points to a home computer with sophisticated access to service centers and hence higher cost.

In both cases there will be frustration, access delays, and technical problems to overcome. The temptation to turn the switch to the Bugs Bunny channel will look very attractive.

Still another interesting, but rarely discussed, issue is that of the presentation and formatting of messages. Video screens are not designed for reading. Even in the culture of systems programming, where instant access to large amounts of structured information is a way of life, there are very few effective tools that use the terminal screen as a way of controlling programs. The typical workstation of the professional programmer is still surrounded with piles of paper listings. There are many reasons for the electronic newspaper community of tomorrow to continue to use the printed page. I have heard Arno Penzies of Bell Laboratories call the printed page "a temporary aberration of technical scarcity." I am not so sure that is the case. *The New York Times*, for instance, has had a great deal of experience both in composing printed pages and in composing information frames for database retrieval. It finds that it takes from half an hour to 2 hours to compose one frame for Videotex, plus about 20 minutes to key it into the system. This assumes, of course, that information is already available and has been reduced to text.

The electronic version of a scientific, technical, or general newspaper is not an easy project. To keep 1000 pages available and updated once a week is a very large operation. Other forms of information dissemination, such as mailbox systems, may not have as many conversion problems, but the fact remains that the medium is not really designed for reading and that color doesn't make the task easier. And live computer conferencing, potentially the most exciting feature of an interactive message service, might be very expensive in an environment where users have to use the phone line for extended periods.

Another interesting service issue is information overload. While the aficionados of Videotex are thrilled at the idea of giving every home direct access to the entire Library of Congress, the concept is a nightmare to anyone trained in information science. Very large amounts of data are generally confusing or misleading to their users, unless there is a controlled mechanism that creates a path through the information by careful use of key words, indexes, and thesauri. To create and utilize these mechanisms represents a massive investment in human skill, money, and time. No electric utility runs a direct line from Hoover Dam to the average American home: The power has to go through transformers and filters before it is ready for the consumer. Access to information resources is likely to follow similar rules. Someone will have to pay for the filtering, the editing, the searching.

At the user end, the thought of access to so much information on so many subjects may be exhilarating for a while, but this feeling may be followed by intense frustration. And computer message systems, if they are not used appropriately, will only add to the confusion. All of us in the field have experienced, at one time or another, the intense need to "disconnect," to reduce participation to only a few selected conferences or user groups, to seek independent channels of information that bypass the computer.

Perhaps the most effective prescription for the intelligent use of message systems is to resist the "addiction" they tend to precipitate, apply them only to clearly defined areas of work where their power is justified and cost-effective, and consider their use from home only when the service they provide makes one's life easier or more pleasant. When these guidelines are followed, message systems can develop to form a new medium for group communications—a new medium for which the growing human community has an intense need.

Case Study 9: An Electronic Journal Sponsored by the British Library

The first "electronic journal" in Europe is now at the testing stage at two British universities. It is using the NOTEPAD system as the basis for all information exchange among the scientists involved.

In September 1980, the British Library awarded grants to Birmingham University and Loughborough University to initiate a new electronic network experiment. Birmingham has received £122,000 and Loughborough £134,000 to establish the hardware and software facilities for the research effort.

The first project in the program is headed by Professor Brian Shackel of the Human Science Department at Loughborough. He is investigating the problems concerned with setting up and using various types of electronic journals. In the words of the British library's press release:

> With the help of suitable software an author may enter a text into a system, and the editor, referees, and ultimately the users, as well as himself, can have access to the text at their computer terminals. The subject of this experimental electronic journal will be "Computer Human Factors"—that is, the science and technology of people interacting with computers.
>
> The contributors to the electronic newspaper will be drawn from UK research establishments. Each will contribute at least one research article and one shorter note in each year of the life of the project, entering the articles on-line to the computer at Birmingham or using other methods, including an optical character recognition reader at Birmingham and a word processor at Loughborough.

These projects use facilities developed at the Computer Center of the University of Birmingham by Professor P. Jarrat and his staff.

The potential importance of electronic journals is increasingly recognized by scientists in view of the rising costs of materials, production, publishing, and library facilities. Experiments such as those in progress at Birmingham may lead to a massive change in the editing, reviewing, and distributing of scientific information in coming years. Researchers will be able to search current journal issues for articles of interest to them and print them out at their terminals, a natural extension of the features of conferencing systems.

The initial community for the British Library electronic journal is composed of scientists working in the human sciences or the computer and information fields. They form the "Loughborough Information Network Community"—or LINC, for short.

In an article published in *Ergonomics* in 1982 (14), Brian Shackel has listed the nine types of electronic journals to be explored during the study; he categorized them as follows:

1 Referred Papers—writing, revision, submission, refereeing, editing, and acceptance of scientific papers.

2 Comments and Discussion—short discussion papers stimulated by an accepted paper which, if accepted, are archived with that paper.

3 Annotated Abstracts or Annotated Bibliography—for organizing purposes, treated as a separate journal. LINC members submit a critical summary of papers they have just read in the open literature relevant to Computer Human Factors (which literature is widely scattered). Less refereeing involved; perhaps one referee only, or perhaps signed by the contributor, and accepted by this journal editor without refereeing.

4 LINC News—as a development from the information letters sent out to LINC members, a regular news sheet will be issued to provide network and related information.

5 Bulletin—again for organizing purposes, treated as a separate journal. LINC members submit quarterly, for quarterly publication, via an open access file, a summary of their recent activities in a lively style. No refereeing. Other relevant information to be taken from other newsletters in Computer Human Factors. Such a bulletin could also be printed out and copied for distribution as a newsletter to a wider community.

6 Cooperative Writing of Papers—e.g., developing a manual. In applied ergonomics for terminal design there is current active work developing manuals and checklists to aid designers, especially those selecting terminals for purchase. Pooling case-study experience from LINC members who use the manual and checklists could lead to faster development and a better end result.

7 Poster Papers—in this type of journal any author can enter any papers and receive comments, and can revise the papers for later offering formally to the refereed papers, electronic journal, or a conventional journal.

8 Enquiry-Answer System between Experts—another type of use allowing any accepted participant to pose specific problems so as to invite expert advice.

9 Readers Only—another category of participants; i.e., noncontributing recipients. It is thought that many scientists and technologists working in university computer studies departments, in commercial manufacturers' and software houses, etc., will become interested in this project and may wish to gain access.

Each member of LINC is expected to submit at least one paper and one short note each year and keep a logbook of related activity and experience at the terminal. An author submits a paper by notifying the editor through the system that his or her paper has been created. The editor then directs it to the appropriate referees, still through the conferencing system. Once the paper has been formally accepted, it is transferred to an archive file, where it is abstracted and indexed. It then becomes available to all LINC members. If it is rejected, the paper stays in the author's own file and may be communicated to others privately.

Although we have already noted that computer message systems were useful to increase access to one's colleagues, a little anecdote helps put this observation in perspective.

After the first 6 months of system use, a researcher made telephone calls to members of LINC to conduct a survey and reached only 24 percent of them with the first call. The obvious conclusion was that the system was needed to enable researchers to be in contact with their peers, if nothing else. In a few years, a much wider population will experience this increased opportunity for access to news, to data, and to the thoughts of other people.

EPILOGUE

The rapid penetration of personal computers into every facet of American life is changing the context of message systems. At home, new educational, financial, entertainment and advertising services are becoming possible, giving the public access to large information resources (15). At work, office structures are being altered to accommodate the impact of computers whose presence is felt through text processing, transaction processing, and exchange of information within the firm.

The technology we have reviewed, then, is only the beginning. Computer message systems will specialize in coming years. They will support activities previously constrained by the use of the telephone, Telex, or mail. Their features will evolve quickly. For this reason we have not devoted a great deal of space to an analysis of the current functions of message systems. The field is evolving too rapidly for a unique set of commands, or a standard user interface, to have developed yet. Instead, we have tried to illustrate and highlight those features that seemed to work best in the early implementations, and to call the attention of the reader to the human and social issues that constrained the message system to a greater degree than the technology did.

For the reader who wishes to pursue the discussion of computer message systems to another level of detail, there are many sources of information (19). There are technical books on networking, covering both local area networks and public networks, including the use of satellites and packet-switching (16). These books give an insight into the development of professional tools that support communications within the workplace.

Similarly, the literature of Videotex is expanding, with a wealth of projections about information resources that can be used from the home (17). These two types of technology will naturally overlap. Some of the more successful implementations of Videotex have been dedicated to business users, and many personal computers are already being used by home users to access the major public networks.

It is perhaps in this last observation that we find the key to the next important developments in message systems. It is not so much the tool itself that matters, but how it is applied. And the most significant applications may turn out to be hybrids, created by entrepreneurs who are not afraid of crossing technological lines to serve well-defined user populations, and satisfy their need for communications (18).

We opened this book with the remark that people rarely bought computers in order to communicate. This state of affairs may change in a few years, with the advent of sophisticated message systems. We have the capability to implement communications systems that are not constrained by time, space, or the number of participants who want access to them. To support such systems may turn out to be the most important role we could assign to computers in the future.

ANNOTATED REFERENCES

1 For a review of audio and video teleconferencing and their relationship to the systems discussed in this book, see *Teleconferencing and Beyond,* by R. Johansen, (New York: *Data Communications,* McGraw-Hill, 1984.)

2 Zipf, G.K.: *Human Behavior* (Cambridge, Mass.: Addison-Wesley, 1949).

3 The author is indebted to Betty Merrill of SRI International for retrieving an article by Massaki Imai describing the managerial implications of high- and low-context cultures. It appeared in the *Japan Economic Journal,* November 30, 1982, p. 12.

4 Costello, Steve: "Are You Ready to Automate Your Office?" Presented at Interface 83. Available from the author at Cities Service Oil and Gas Co., P.O. Box 300, Tulsa, Oklahoma, 74102. The methodology will be expanded in Costello's forthcoming book, *Improving Office Productivity.*

5 Mattox, Addie: "Office Automation to Enhance Productivity in an R&D Environment," Munchner Kreis Congress, May 1983.

6 Myer and Dodds: "Notes on the Development of Message Technology," in *Proceedings,* Berkeley Workshop on Distributed Data Management, May 1976.

7 Turoff, M., and Hiltz, R.: *The Network Nation* (Reading, Mass.: Addison-Wesley, 1978).

8 Pittinger, R., Hockett, C., and Daheny, J.: "The First Five Minutes: A Sample of Microscopic Interview Analysis" (Ithaca, N.Y.: Paul Martineau, 1960).

9 Schneidman, E.: *The Logics of Communication: A Manual for Analysis* (China Lake, Calif.: US Naval Ordnance Test Station, 1966).

10 Laffal, J.: *Pathological and Normal Language* (New York: Atherton Press).
On the same subject, see also: "Contextual Similarities as a Basis of Inference," in George Gerbner, *The Analysis of Communication Content* (New York: John Wiley, 1969).

11 Much of the material in this section is based on an unpublished study by Arthur Hastings, who applied this technique to the analysis of transcripts of several research conferences.

12 Vallee, J., et al.: Letter to the editor, *Science,* April 18, 1975, p. 203. See also Kupperman, Wilcox, and Smith: "Crisis Management—Some Opportunities," *Science,* February 7, 1975, pp. 404–410.

13 Noll, Michael: "Teletext and Videotext in North America," *Telecommunications Policy,* March 1980.

14 Shackel, B.: "The BLEND System: Programme for the Study of Some Electronic Journals," *Ergonomics,* 25 , No. 4, p. 269.

15 There are more than 450 computer bulletin board systems (CBBS) in the United States and Canada at this writing. All of them are free. The user is responsible for telephone charges only. There is a directory of available CBBS called the *On-Line Computer Telephone Directory.* It is available from the OLCTD Subscription Department, P.O. Box 10005, Kansas City, Mo., 64111. Four issues a year for $9.95.

16 For an up-to-date description of network technology see Roy Rosner: *Distributed Telecommunciations Networks* (Belmont, Calif.: Lifetime Learning Publications, 1982).

17 Tydeman, J., et al.: *Teletext and Videotext in the United States* (New York: Data *Communications,* McGraw-Hill, 1982).

18 Johansen, R., Vallee, J., and Vian, Kathleen: *Electronic Meetings: Technical Alternatives and Social Choices* (Reading, Mass.: Addison-Wesley, 1979).

19 Up-to-date information regarding new offerings in computer message systems is available from the Electronic Mail Association (EMA), 1919 Pennsylvania Avenue NW, Suite 300, Washington, D.C. 20006. Telephone (202) 293-7808, Mr. Michael Cavanaugh, Executive Director. The International Federation for Information Processing (IFIP) has formed a working group (WG6.5) dealing with computer-based message systems.

20 Nothhaft, Henry: "Making a Case for Using Electronic Mail," *Data Communications,* May 1982. A detailed presentation of electronic mail features.

INDEX

INDEX